MW00647065

Craft to Heal

Soothing Your Soul with Sewing,
Painting, and Other Pastimes

To Stephanie,
Be creative!

Nancy Monson

NANCY MONSON

Craft to Heal:
Soothing Your Soul with Sewing, Painting,
and Other Pastimes

Copyright © 2011 Nancy Monson. All rights reserved. No part
of this book may be reproduced or retransmitted in any form or
by any means without the written permission of the publisher.

Cover illustration *Letting Go: Gaia Series* A9 Lura Schwarz
Smith, 60" x 72", www.lura-art.com.

Photo by Kerby C. Smith. Used with permission.

Published by Hats Off Books
610 East Delano Street, Suite 104
Tucson, Arizona 85705 U.S.A.
www.hatsoffbooks.com

International Standard Book Number 10: 1-58736-425-5
International Standard Book Number 13: 978-1-58736-425-9
Library of Congress Control Number: 2004117113

rev201101

To my mother, Barbara Peckel, because she taught me to craft.

And to my sister, Linda Peckel, for being my friend, for always being there for me, and for contributing so much to this book.

Thank you both.

Contents

Part I: Crafts and Healing

Part II: How to Reap the Healing Benefits of Crafts

Acknowledgments

A special note of gratitude to Lura Schwarz Smith, who graciously allowed me to use her incredible quilt on the cover of the book. As soon as I saw it, I knew it belonged with my words. Another special thanks to Gail McMeekin, a dear friend and a constant support and cheerleader. Gail, you have touched me deeply with your warmth and encouragement. Thank you to all of my crafting friends and acquaintances who shared their stories, enthusiasm, and work, and to the wonderful artists, crafters, and experts who talked with me about this topic so close to my heart and soul. Finally, a thank you to Linda Konner for her efforts.

Part I

Crafts and Healing

The Surprising Connection between Crafts, Creativity, and Healing

Time heals all wounds. But until time kicks in, what do you do while you're waiting? How do you relieve stress and decompress from everyday pressures? How do you ease the pain, distract your mind, soothe your soul? If you're like me—and I suspect you are—you craft.

I've been a crafter for as long as I can remember. I quilt. I sew. I collage. I paint. I make wreaths. I design note cards. I love to create something out of nothing and put my personal stamp on it. I love the process, and I love the product. The creative arts, my crafts, keep my hands, heart, and mind busy, and sometimes I think they're the only things that keep me sane. And I'm not alone. Far from it. In fact, from the time that man began recording time, the creative arts have been used as unique forms of expression, communication, and release. Just think of the stick figures found on the cave walls of our earliest ancestors, the decorative vases molded by ancient Chinese cultures, or the ornate tombs of the early Egyptians. Now, in the twenty-first century, these arts have been elevated from mere crafts to important components of healing therapies for people with illnesses, both physical and psychological. Patients with cancer, for instance, are encouraged to paint, to visualize their bodies fighting off malignant cells, and to pour their thoughts and emotions into journals. Likewise, abused children are asked to draw pictures to help therapists gain access to their feelings and fears. Arts and crafts are even used as part of the therapeutic rehabilitation of prisoners, the disabled, the mentally disadvantaged, and those with substance abuse problems, and to engage the elderly and people with dementia.

"Some of us feel bad about [taking] time for creative expression. One would think that we'd view creativity as 'more productive' and hence less guilt-producing than leisure, yet we still seem to believe that self-expression is less of a priority than satisfying the needs of others."

—Alice Domar, PhD, Self-Nurture

But the best news is that you don't have to be ill to benefit. "We're now finding that crafts are beneficial for healthy people, too," says Gail McMeekin, MSW, a career and creativity coach in Massachusetts, and the author of the inspiring books *The 12 Secrets of Highly Creative Women* and *The 12 Secrets of Highly Successful Women.* "Thanks to their ability to tune you into yourself and your feelings, crafts clearly have physical, psychological, and spiritual powers." Adds Diane Ericson, a California fabric artist, teacher, and pattern designer, "Crafts are a way of valuing yourself and giving to yourself. They allow you to express what's inside."

That's right: Crafts are no longer perceived as kitschy activities for clueless country bumpkins. They're now considered cool, part of the do-it-yourself movement, shared by celebrities and funky young chicks from Brooklyn, New York, middle-aged women, and yes, even men.

> *"All serious daring starts from within."*
>
> —Eudora Welty

The Study of Crafting

In case you need more proof of crafting's popularity, just visit your local Jo-Ann's, Michael's, or AC Moore's, and you'll find the stores are packed. Crafting is a $29-billion industry in America, and over half of Americans have tried it, according to the Craft and Hobby Association. What's more, crafting has held strong through the recent recession—in fact, as many Americans have turned to crafts and hobbies to save money on gifts as they have because they find crafts to be a potent form of stress relief.

America's Most Popular Pastimes

1. Drawing
2. Scrapbooking and memory crafts
3. Crocheting
4. Woodworking/wood crafts
5. Jewelry-making
6. Card-making
7. Floral decorating
8. Cross-stitch
9. Knitting
10. Wreath-making

Source: Craft and Hobby Association

The Stats on Crafts and Hobbies

Amount spent on crafts and hobbies annually	$29.2 billion
Percentage of households that have crafted at least once during the past year	56%
Most popular craft	Drawing
Why people craft	For the sense of accomplishment, relaxation and stress relief, memory-keeping, health, economy/value, recommended by friends or family, social opportunity, and interaction with children

Source: Craft and Hobby Association

Despite crafting's popularity, researchers haven't spent much time exploring its benefits. Luckily, there is one landmark study—one that was deemed important enough to be mentioned in the prestigious *Journal of the American Medical Association*. In the study, which was sponsored by the Home Sewing Association, researchers took thirty women (fifteen experienced sewers and fifteen novice sewers) and measured their blood pressures, heart rates, perspiration rates, and skin temperatures—all gauges of stress—via biofeedback before and after they performed five leisure activities that required similar eye-hand movements. The pastimes included sewing a simple project, playing a card game, painting at an easel, playing a handheld video game, and reading a newspaper. The results showed that sewing was the most relaxing activity of the five studied; it produced drops in heart rate, blood pressure, and perspiration. In contrast, stress measures *increased* after the women performed the other tasks, especially after playing a card or video game.

According to Robert Reiner, PhD, a New York University psychologist and the study's author, the findings prove what crafters already know: crafts de-stress. "The act of performing a craft is incompatible with worry, anger, obsession, and anxiety," he says. "Crafts make you concentrate and focus on the here and now and distract you from everyday pressures and problems. They're stress-busters in the same way that meditation, deep breathing, visual imagery, and watching fish are."

Harvard University's world-renowned mind/body expert, Herbert Benson, MD, says that repetitive and rhythmic crafts such as knitting may even evoke what he calls the relaxation response—a feeling of bodily and mental calm that's been scientifically proven to enhance health and reduce the risk of heart disease, anxiety, and depression. "You can induce the relaxation response through any type of repetition, whether it's repeating a word, prayer, or action, such as knitting or sewing," he notes. "The act of doing a task over and over again breaks the train of everyday thought, and that's what releases stress."

"Hide not your talents. They for use were made. What's a sundial in the shade?"

—Benjamin Franklin

Unfortunately, many of us push crafting and creativity to the bottom of our "to do" list. Maybe we feel guilty for doing something for ourselves—women, of course, are taught that everyone else's needs should come first—or maybe we feel that even when we're relaxing, we should be doing something productive (that old multitasking thing). But now that research is showing the creative arts are good for our health and relationships, we no longer need to view leisure pursuits as self-indulgences. We can recast them in a new light: crafts aren't just enjoyable, they're *downright therapeutic*.

"Each of us has our own way of expressing ourselves. Each of us has something special to give. And it is important to value our own way of expressing ourselves—whatever it is."

—Sue Bender, Stretching Lessons

Letting In the Power of Crafts

In interviewing creative women for her first book, Gail McMeekin learned that there are no mistakes in creating, only lessons. "Many inventions are the result of so-called errors," she says. "When you suspend judgment about what is and what isn't a mistake, you open your mind to creating extraordinary things and to receiving extraordinary things too. You let in the healing power of crafts."

I've experienced this power firsthand on many occasions, but especially when I began making a quilt that I ended up calling "My Divorce Quilt" in the summer of 2000. I was taking a workshop that explored the use of decorative threads on quilt tops. I don't know why—perhaps because the technique of embellishing was so new to me—but I decided to give myself permission to make up the quilt as I went along. I had no real plan, which is not the way I usually work at all. Most of my quilts follow a pattern and are somewhat uniform and regimented (see photos 1 and 2), and I'm hounded by a desire for perfection. But this time I didn't try to make all of the elements work together. I just did what I wanted, spontaneously sewing this way and that according to whim, ignoring the usual conventions and restraints, and letting errors become planned eccentricities instead.

First, I pieced together two hundred small batik squares into a larger square shape. Then I played with the thread for hours—days, really—creating geometric shapes across the quilt top. Next, I highlighted the shapes with variegated yarns. Finally, I began to machine quilt in a most verboten way: putting flowers and curly-cues next to squares, triangles, and other angular shapes. I even used whatever color thread I picked up first, without caring if it matched the fabric or not.

"Every child is an artist. The problem is how to remain an artist once he grows up."

—Pablo Picasso

I was bold and in the process. I was unconcerned about the end result and often put aside the quilt to look at it and search for inspiration while I worked on other pieces. This, too, was unusual for me, since I typically rush to finish one project and start another on my ever-expanding list of quilts I want to make. I was moving beyond the constraints of doing things "the right way" (which I had applied to my life and my quilting) to just seeing where the project would take me. Suddenly, screwing up was just a way of discovering something new.

1. Some of the pattern-oriented quilts I've made.

2. A watercolor quilt, pieced block
by tiny block (again, coloring
inside the lines!).

As I worked on the quilt over several weeks, I began to see that the evolving design was expressing some of the chaos and confusion I was feeling as I went through my divorce. And as I neared the end of the project, I was overwhelmed (or perhaps underwhelmed) by the finished product. The quilt was a busy and disheartening mishmash. I entertained the idea of slicing it up and repiecing it. Unable to bring myself to actually cut into a piece I'd spent so many hours sewing, I was inspired instead to fold it several times on the diagonal and tack it down. And I loved the way it looked—it now has a kind of mangled, arrow shape to it, which is entirely appropriate to its purpose. It looks like it has been through an antique washing machine—just as I felt I, as a human being, had been—so I renamed it "My Divorce Quilt: Through the Wringer" (see photo 3).

Of all of my quilts—and I've made over one hundred—this one has elicited the biggest and most dramatic response from people who view it. When I hung it in my guild's quilt show, it created a buzz among the attendees. One woman told me that she thought the folds were my way of trying to tuck away memories of my marriage. She even suggested that I might feel compelled to fold it further as time passed, signifying my healing from the divorce and my moving on to a new life. I was fascinated by this insight and suddenly realized that I had created my first art quilt! Whatever I had made—and it certainly wasn't a typical quilt—expressed something deep inside of me. And this quilt definitely *says* something, not only to me, but to others. Making it and showing it has helped me to heal the chasm in my life and to feel whole again, this time as a single person. And it turned out to be a message to myself that it was time for me to pursue life without a strict adherence to a plan. Since then, I've opened up creatively and emotionally to exploring life in general as more of a process, and enjoying the twists and turns, rather than just rushing to the goal.

That is the gift of crafts. They can transport us to another place and help us in our journey through life. They can heal our souls, if we allow them to. All we need is permission from ourselves to spend time creating and the courage to push beyond our comfort zone so that our projects truly express what's inside and help us to unblock, purge, and transform our feelings. And if I can do it, you can too.

3. "My Divorce Quilt: Through the Wringer."
No plan, I just winged it—and my first
art quilt was the result!

Healing Lesson

Scientific research is beginning to reveal
what crafters have intuitively known all
along—that crafts have mental, physical,
and spiritual benefits.

The Stress
Connection—It's
All About Attitude

2

If life constructs stress, then crafts help to deconstruct it. For Nancy Green-Keyes, who makes ornately detailed decoupage mirrors, book boxes, and furniture, her craft is the perfect stress antidote to a hectic job as a Hollywood casting director for movies such as *The Notebook, Family Man,* and *Rush Hour.* "Decoupage is like a minivacation from my life," she says. "It empties my head, and I don't think about personal or work problems. I don't answer the phone. I just focus on what I'm creating and the precision of my craft."

The Dripping Tap

Ironically, psychologists say that it's the daily small stresses that are most deleterious to our health, not the large stresses, such as catastrophic accidents or illnesses. "We think of stress in relation to dramatic events, such as death, disaster, and divorce," says University of Montreal psychologist Ethel Roskies, PhD, author of *Stress Management for the Healthy Type A.* "People think they should be able to handle great amounts of stress and be able to shrug it off," she explains, "but it's the dripping tap that drives you crazy, not the flood."

What's more, doctors say it's not the actual events themselves that make us uptight—it's the way we react to them. In reality, how stress affects you depends largely on how much control you feel you have over your life, how stressful you perceive situations to be, and how you respond to them.

"I feel that art has something to do with the achievement of stillness in the midst of chaos. A stillness which characterizes prayer, too, and the eye of the storm. I think that art has something to do with the arrest of attention in the midst of distraction."

—Saul Bellow

The Effects of Stress

When stress mounts, a chain of involuntary physiological responses begins. This is called the fight-or-flight response, and it's an emergency reaction dating back to caveman times, when humans had to either fight or run away when faced with a stressor (usually a large, life-threatening animal). To give the body the wherewithal to fight or run, blood pressure, breathing, and heart rate increase, and stress hormones (such as cortisol and adrenaline) are released. Today, we're rarely faced with situations where we have to fight or flee. But we do encounter constant, small stresses and larger, more taxing stresses that trigger this involuntary bodily reaction without our even knowing it. Since we neither fight nor flee, we carry the stress around with us. Over time, the reaction has dire consequences, depleting the body's immune system, raising cholesterol levels, damaging brain cells, and setting the stage for heart attacks, strokes, diseases, and other ailments.

When you're ...	Try ...
Sad	Quilting or sewing, because the bright colors of the fabrics can improve your mood, or drawing in a journal with colored pencils, because expressive art can help you release negative emotions.
Anxious	Knitting, crocheting, and cross-stitch, because the repetition of movement can relax you. Beading is another good choice: the meticulous nature of this craft won't allow you to think of anything else.
Reflective/ pensive	Scrapbooking or collaging, because it gives you a chance to recall key moments in your life. Or try photography, which allows you to compose as you go.
Angry	Ceramics, sculpting, metal crafts, gardening, and other highly physical crafts, because they can help you get out your aggressions.

Despite all this, stress isn't always a bad thing. When present in manageable doses, it can be a great motivator. After all, deadline pressure for a craft show is what forces you to finish a project. Too little stress and life is uneventful; too much and it's exasperating and dangerous. The path to stress resiliency is striking a balance—learning how to push yourself enough so that you're the best you can be, but not so much that you go through life harried and unhappy.

Life is very short and very uncertain;
let us spend it as well as we can.

—Samuel Johnson

The Three Stress Profiles

We don't all feel stress equally—and some of us may not think we feel it at all! Researchers have identified three basic stress profiles, one of which probably fits you (although you may also have some of the characteristics of another type).

- **Type As.** We know them as classic overachievers. They're competitive, driven, and energetic. They're also very time-conscious and prone to anger and arguments.

- **Type Bs.** These are easygoing pleasure-seekers. They're uncomfortable with responsibility and are great delegators.

- **Type Cs.** Pleasant to a fault, these people hold in negative emotions and are easily taken advantage of by others because they have trouble asserting themselves.

Because of their behavior styles, Type As and Cs are subject to long-term stress—often every day, all day. Type Bs, on the other hand, suffer only periodic stress, largely because they're quick to remove themselves from stressful situations.

Breaking the Stress Habit

Before you get all stressed out over your type, remember that it's merely a behavior pattern, a coping style, not a permanent personality trait. You *can* change the way you handle life's curveballs. Here's how to do it with a little help from crafts.

Type As

Learn to choose your battles. Know when to rise to a challenge and when to back down. This requires you to become more aware of stress triggers, pace yourself, and learn specific coping and time-management skills. For instance, if your mother-in-law has a habit of frequently insulting you, instead of lashing back, pick up your knitting needles and "vent" your frustration on them. You'll be surprised at how much better you'll feel.

Stress-buster: Because Type As are antsy, you need to release your aggressions. Seek out active relaxation techniques—running and swimming—rather than passive meditative-like activities. Perhaps woodworking, photography, or other active pastimes might be good crafts for you to try.

Type Bs

The trick for Type Bs is to recognize that, although you probably think you're immune to most stress, you too are affected. You're at risk for avoidance behavior and may try to cover up a problem with a quick fix. Make sure you're not ignoring sensitive issues or pretending they don't exist—you may suddenly explode when the stress catches up with you.

Stress-buster: Since you're probably more social than other types, group activities, such as making a quilt with others, scrapbooking, team sports, or a dance class, may work well for you.

Type Cs

Learning to release your emotions is the secret to stress reduction for you. You might benefit from assertiveness training. Work on graciously saying no to others' demands and asking for support when you're feeling overwhelmed. You keep much of your stress pent up and you're at risk of boiling over.

Stress-buster: Meditation, deep breathing, and other "quiet" stress-reducers are sure bets for your type, as are rhythmic crafts such as knitting, crocheting, sewing, and ceramics (throwing pots on a wheel). Keeping a visual or a written journal can help you access repressed emotions.

Stressed Out?
Take a Creative Vacation!

Gas, food, and travel prices have been high for the past few years, which means many people are having a hard time finding the cash to take a trip for the summer or the holidays. But just because you can't find the funds to travel to a far-off destination doesn't mean you should skip your vacation. There are far too many benefits of taking a break from work—reducing tension and depression, stoking motivation and problem-solving abilities, and improving sleep to name a few—to forego it.

In fact, why not take a *creative vacation* right at home? There are great stress-reducing perks to self-expression—letting your imagination run free and your hands bring something new and unique into being. Just don't tackle something TOO big or complicated, or you'll end up more frazzled than relaxed.

Here's how to get started:

- **Explore a hobby you've always been interested in but never had the time to delve into before.** It may be photography or ceramics, flower arranging, decoupage, cake decorating, sewing, or painting. Whatever sparks your interest, you can find supplies and instructions at national craft chains such as Jo-Ann's, Michael's, or AC Moore's. Likewise, take a one-day class, buy a video, or join a group of similar enthusiasts. You may even be able to find discounts on classes through Groupon, Get Social, or other web-based discounting groups.
- **Make gifts for the holidays.** Gifts made by the giver can have great meaning and value for recipients—and ease the impact on your pocketbook. So pull out your stack of photos and start a scrapbook or collage for your Mom. Grab the knitting needles and get clicking on a sweater for your Dad. Create a bracelet for your aunt. Kits can be had at your local craft stores or you can pick and choose supplies and embellishments individually.
- **Try out some of those recipes you've been collecting.**

Many of us love to clip recipes from magazines but infrequently get around to making new dishes. So dedicate your vacation this year to a cookfest! Or use your time off to learn how the bread-maker or home brewing system you got as a gift works.

- **Make your clothes look like new with embellishments.** If you can't afford to buy new clothes, make the ones you've got look not only refreshed but trendy with embellishments such as fabric paint, Swarovski crystals, and embroidery. There are reams of websites, books, and magazines such as *Ready Made and Make it Mine* to help you accomplish the task. If you're really ambitious, you may even want to tackle making a garment from scratch.

- **Invite friends over for a craft day.** One of the joys of creativity is that it can be shared, with the double benefit that socializing is good for our health and well-being. So ask friends over to spend the day making jewelry or scrapping, enlist them to repaint your kitchen, or do a craft project with the kids. You might even attempt a group project. Quilters, for instance, engage in quilting round-robins, where each quilter is called upon to add a unique element to a quilt block before passing it along to another. The resulting quilt is often given to charity. Alternatively, plan a group trip to an art museum or cultural event. Being in creative surroundings can often spark *your* creative urges.

Healing Lesson

Different kinds of crafts can be used
to relieve different types of stressful
feelings, and depending on your
particular stress profile you may enjoy
some types of crafts more than others.

The Crafter's Orientation: Knowing Your Brain Type

The way your brain works may not seem to have much to do with creativity. After all, intellect and creativity appear to come from two different places. But the fact is, your brain actually has two distinct ways of seeing and perceiving the world (we know this from something called "split-brain" research), and these perspectives influence not only how you approach crafts, but the fun you have with them.

In the now-classic book *Drawing on the Right Side of the Brain,* art professor Dr. Betty Edwards talks about how the dual nature of the brain affects the artistic process. She notes that the left side, which governs the physical functions of the opposite (right) side of the body, is the logical, highly structured side, while the right side, which controls the physical functions of the left side of the body, is the creative, free-spirited side.

Most of us naturally favor one side of the brain over the other and may even try to suppress the opposing brain style, thinking it's bad or wrong. Traditionally, left-brained approaches have been favored in schools and business and by society in general, because they get the job done. Right-brained strategies have been viewed as less desirable—immature, flighty, and unfocused. But split-brain research has found that both sides are important to healthy

How the Two Halves of Your Brain See Things

Left Brain	Right Brain
Verbal (thinks in language)	Imagistic (thinks in images)
Analytic (figures things out step-by-step)	Synthesizes information to form wholes
Ordered/planned/structured	Flexible/unpredictable
Rational/serious	Playful
Sequential/serial/linear	Spontaneous
Objective	Subjective
Aware of time	Forgets about time
Detail-oriented	Sees the big picture
Logical/deals with facts	Intuitive/goes on hunches
Symbolic/abstract	Oriented to the present moment
Domineering/controlling	Easygoing

Sources: *Drawing on the Right Side of the Brain* by Betty Edwards and *You Don't Have to Go Home from Work Exhausted!* by Ann McGee-Cooper

functioning (and to creation, because without the left brain butting in you'd never finish a project!). Fighting your brain's natural inclination can be time-consuming and unproductive, as well as extremely frustrating.

According to Barbara Ganim, an expressive arts therapist and the author of *Art and Healing: Using Expressive Art to Heal Your Body, Mind and Spirit*, the important research finding about the split brain also reveals that the primary language of the body is imagistic, or governed by the right side of the brain. It's not verbal. "We think and process our experiences, feelings and emotions as images first and words second," she writes in her book. "The body's senses and the right side of the brain take in all of our experiences and the corresponding emotions as images first, and then the left side of the brain translates those images into verbal thoughts." This is why crafts are so potent for healing: as visual art forms, they communicate in the body's internal language of images to access and release the deepest feelings.

"Getting to know both sides of your brain is an important step in liberating your creative potential."

—Betty Edwards, Drawing on the Right Side of the Brain

By design, the left brain is domineering and likes to take over any task at hand. That means that most of us, and especially those with a natural leaning toward the left brain, have to learn ways to bring forth the right brain and allow it free reign. One way to access your right brain is to unleash your imagination by listening to music, taking a walk, or practicing a relaxation technique, such as progressive relaxation, yoga, or meditation. These activities help you ease into a laid-back, quiet state that opens the channels leading to crafter's nirvana (joy and complete engrossment), and allow for creative discoveries.

Brain Integration and Creativity on the Job

"Mixing left- and right-brain skills is more important than ever in today's business world," says Connie Thanasoulis Cerrachio, co-founder of Six Figure Start, a success coaching firm. "Innovation is king, and young and old employees alike are looking to reinvent themselves in the face of a changing job market." Linear, serial thinking, analytical skills, and discipline are still highly desirable qualities in an employee, but increasingly it's important for that same employee to be able to come up with out-of-the-box solutions to business problems. One company exemplifies this trend: Apple, with its leader Steve Jobs, and its astoundingly innovative products from the iPod to the iPhone and the iPad. As *USA Today* writer Marco R. della Cava notes, "Fusing left-brain skills with right-brain insights is considered the killer app in a new economy that will put a premium on creative breakthroughs."

"Getting to know both sides of your brain is an important step in liberating your creative potential," writes Betty Edwards. Both sides function in a highly sophisticated manner, but think, perceive, and reason in disparate ways. The two sides can operate singly— or even against one another. But the goal is to get them to work together, integrating the two sides into a whole and drawing from the strengths of each to free your artistic talents.

Healing Lesson

Split-brain research suggests that
fighting your natural brain orientation
(particularly if you're left-brained) is
a bad idea, and will lead to crafting
frustration and disappointment. Rather,
the route to creative success and de-
stressing lies in drawing from both sides
of the brain and their complementary
ways of perceiving and thinking.

Creativity, Schmativity—We All Can Do It!

When I hear the word *creative*, I conjure up visions of great masters at work—Pablo Picasso, Auguste Renoir, Claude Monet, Georgia O'Keefe—and somehow my name doesn't resonate with theirs. But the truth is that all human beings are creative—meaning simply that they have the ability to develop something out of nothing or to bring something into being. In more artistic terms, they have the capacity to manifest in a tangible form their emotions, dreams, and aspirations, and to reinvent themselves and their lives.

The trouble is that many people believe they're not really creative, or they're only marginally creative (you got me there), perhaps because they follow patterns or copy others' work (a classic learning technique, by the way, and a means by which all beginners acquire technique). Or they think they're not creative because they "just do crafts," not real artwork. But no matter what you create, no matter how pedestrian or simple, you obviously make choices—about what pattern to use, the materials to work with, how to start, how to fix errors—and these choices are the very essence of creativity. And when you begin to take your craft and make it into something more self-expressive, the line between commonplace crafting and art gets blurred. Suddenly, an everyday craft like painting a wooden birdhouse becomes art.

> "Creativity is a journey, not a destination."
>
> —Gail McMeekin

"Every kind of creativity
depends on our
ability to play"

—Alice Domar, PhD,
Self-Nurture

It's also true that creativity isn't confined to just the discipline of painting. It can take the form of making music, cooking up a storm, problem-solving on the job, or tackling a project from a fresh or unique angle. "The need to create is just a part of the human package," says quilt artist Lura Schwarz Smith. "I believe we're all happier and more complete if we allow ourselves the empowerment of the creative act. The way in which we explore our creativity isn't important—in the garden, in the kitchen, in the established arts, crafts, music, or dance—the important thing is the process."

Conversely, the absence of a creative outlet in our lives can have a deleterious effect on our health and well-being. The Women's Health Study, a large medical trial funded by the National Institutes of Health, for instance, recently found that women who have stressful jobs that don't allow them the latitude to make decisions or to be creative have a higher risk of heart attack than women whose jobs are less taxing. In short, this suggests that living an art-less life can kill you!

An Interview
with Julia Cameron

Creativity Teacher and Author of *The Artist's Way:*
A Spiritual Path to Higher Creativity

How do you define creativity?

Creativity is a personal, spiritual energy. Each soul is a creation, and in turn, is intended to create. In our culture, we have a limiting view of creativity, tending to categorize it as relating only to the fine arts. This is untrue. All of life is an arena for creative practice. Every choice we make is a chance to exercise our creativity.

Many people believe they are not truly creative (they're not "real" artists). Do you think that's true? Is creativity inborn or learned, or a bit of both?

All people are creative. Creativity is a part of what I call our "spiritual DNA." Some people are more comfortable with their creativity. They may come from a nurturing background or simply have a very strong creative drive. The important point is that all of us can become more comfortable with our creativity and more expressive within it. The tools that I teach are like gardening tools: the seed is there, we need to help it grow. This is what my tools do.

I've heard you say that "to make art, you must be soft

enough to be hurt by criticism or reviews." Why is that?

The part of us that creates is very open and childlike. This vulnerable, inner youngster has the gift of heartfelt enthusiasm. By the same token, it can be easily hurt. If we lose our vulnerability to pain, we shut down important aspects of empathy that are necessary for creation.

Do you believe that expressing your creative impulses through crafts can have physical, emotional, and spiritual benefits?

Anytime we access our creativity, we become more beautiful spiritually. Not so long ago, people intuitively knew this when they would talk about the benefits of having a hobby. At this time, a young composer I know is working with needlepoint. I can see how this craft both relaxes and focuses her mind. Each day, as the beauty beneath her fingers grows, so too does her balance and equilibrium in her composing art, and in her life.

Why do you believe that creativity is "listening with the inner ear to the heart"?

Many people mistakenly think of creativity as a disembodied intellectual process, an act of the ego that has to do with being smart. In my experience, creativity has more to do with receptivity. We listen to what wants to be made. We become available as conduits for this creation to move into the world. We open our hearts like a welcoming hearth with creativity as the guest.

In your workshops, you give lots of examples of how you've had creative breakthroughs—for instance, how whole songs suddenly came to you while driving your car, or how your intuition told you to go to Taos and buy a house there. How can other people learn to be as receptive to their creative impulses as you are?

Both spirituality and creativity are a form of listening. There are activities, such as "morning pages" [writing freehand in a journal every morning], guided writing, and walking that encourage us to listen more deeply. For over two decades now, I have engaged in these spiritual practices, and practice makes, if not perfect, at least better.

Finally, do you have any thoughts on how we can change our attitudes toward crafting, so we can not only do work that is truly creative, but so we can push through our fear of failure?

It is important to separate the process of the work that we do from the product that is produced for the marketplace. This is not to say that our work will not sell. It is simply a matter of focus and clarity. As we learn to enjoy our craft for the sake of our craft, we become more original, more an origin from which authentic work springs. In a sense, we fall in love with ourselves and our own creative leanings. We take delight in what personally satisfies us. Ironically, as our work becomes more personal, it becomes more universal as well.

> "Imagination is more important than knowledge."
>
> —Albert Einstein

What about Talent?

It's often been said that you're either born with talent for a particular craft or you're not. You can't learn it. Not so, say creativity experts. "Actually, many people mistake a technical skill for talent," says fabric artist and creativity coach Diane Ericson. Talent is a natural affinity for a craft. It isn't the key to creativity. It won't give you a leg up on the competition; it won't help you master all the technical ins and outs of a particular craft, skill, or medium. That can only come with practice and experimentation. Talent may give you a unique flair, but it won't push you to move beyond the ordinary. What's far more important is working

> "Nothing in the world can take the place of persistence. Talent will not; nothing is more common than unsuccessful men with talent. Genius will not; unrewarded genius is almost a proverb. Education alone will not; the world is full of educated derelicts. Persistence and determination alone are omnipotent."
>
> —Anonymous

at your craft, making mistakes, learning from those mistakes, and growing with your work. Courage and perseverance are the names of the crafts game, whether you're doing it for self-expression or for your well-being (and aren't they the same thing?). As Aristotle said, "We are what we repeatedly do. Excellence, then, is not an act, but a habit."

Taking the Leap

So what does real creativity entail? How do you find the true artist that lies within you? "In large measure, being an artist consists of learning to accept yourself, which makes your work personal,

"Your creativity is waiting for you like a dancing partner."

—Barbara Sher

and in following your own voice, which makes your work distinctive," write David Bayles and Ted Orland, the authors of an exhilarating little book called *Art & Fear: Observations on the Perils (and Rewards) of Artmaking.*

The risk, of course, of being a true artist is that you expose your deepest feelings, thoughts, and values, and you risk the ridicule, judgment, and misinterpretation of others. This act of creative bravery is what *O, The Oprah Magazine* columnist Martha Beck calls "embracing your inner brat." It's only when you can push away your shame, fear, and insecurities and say with confidence, "I don't care what anyone else thinks, I'm going to do this my way," that you can let fly what lies within and create something that is truly unique, truly expressive of you, and ultimately truly healing.

If you're one of the legions of people who believe they're not really creative, the first step may simply be to take the risk of saying you want to explore your creativity. Saying yes to crafts—even if that step scares you, even if you're afraid your worst fears about your "lack" of talent will be confirmed—will still show you the inventiveness of your heart and soul. You may not be bowled over by your first attempts, but you're likely to be surprised by how much you like the process. And if you already know that you do indeed have a creative bone in your body (and possibly more than one), nurturing that gift by pursuing a craft will only make you feel better about yourself, securing you a little pocket of your life where you're sure to feel joy.

"Art is about self-acceptance," says Jeanne Carbonetti, a Vermont watercolor artist and the author of a series of books on drawing and painting (see Appendix). "The creative process is infallible. It works perfectly in all of us. Art shows us our beauty—and beauty shows us we are whole, though we may not know it."

Growing your creativity as a means of healing yourself from within…that's what art is about. The challenge is to see that the possibilities abound if you're willing to take the risk.

Healing Lesson

We're all born creative, no ifs, ands, or buts, and that creativity can be expressed in the traditional arts and crafts, or in other ways, such as in the garden or the office. Nurturing your creativity is an ongoing process and one that requires a little bit of guts to say, "This is what I made, like it or not."

The Psychological Benefits of Crafting

Ask most crafters what they get from their craft and they'll inevitably tell you they find it relaxing, therapeutic, and soothing. "How can you worry when you are totally focused on your art? [Crafting] frees my mind, centers and calms me," says Sally Hickerson of Asheville, North Carolina, who makes art-to-wear garments, dolls, and beaded jewelry. So true.

But the mental benefits of having a craft seem to go beyond just stress reduction. For instance, a survey of one thousand individuals, conducted by the Home Sewing Association (HSA), found that sewers are 22 percent more likely to describe themselves as "creative," 9 percent more likely to characterize themselves as "energetic," and 7 percent more likely to call themselves "optimistic" than nonsewers. And despite the lack of leisure time in America, almost one in five Americans pursues sewing as a hobby, according to the HSA.

"It is only through creative activity that any individual can define his own understanding of the world and his place in it."

—Frank Wilson, MD, The Hand

The reasons: the craft gives them a feeling of accomplishment and satisfaction, relaxes them, and provides a connection to children or

37

friends. Many even view sewing and other crafts as a form of self-help therapy.

The Psychological Benefits of Crafting

- ✧ Relieves stress
- ✧ Helps you relax
- ✧ Distracts you from worries and from mindless or emotional eating
- ✧ Gives you a feeling of achievement
- ✧ Raises your self-esteem
- ✧ Provides an opportunity to examine your inner feelings and express them
- ✧ Boosts your mood
- ✧ Can be shared with others (friends, children)

For instance, for Jenny Harwager, of Brush, Colorado, making angel ornaments was a way of coping with the death of her baby boy Logan, from sudden infant death syndrome (SIDS) in 1997. "My arms ached to hold Logan after he died," says Jenny, the mother of two other children. "Doing something with my hands distracted me from that physical sensation—and from the grief I was feeling." When she started to sell her angel ornaments at local craft shows, it also helped her to raise both awareness of SIDS and money for the cause. (She donates the proceeds from her sales to the SIDS Foundation.) "At first, making the angels gave me a sense of purpose and a reason to go on. Now, it helps me to remember Logan in a good way, without the hurt. And it helps me to share my love for him with others."

Margo Martin, of the American Sewing Guild, says that sewing is a "Zen experience" that relaxes and energizes her at the same time. "The hum of the machine, putting my hand to the cloth, and creating art stimulates me so much that it takes me to another place," she says. "I get so involved in my projects I can work through the night!"

Sometimes your choice of craft and craft supplies can offer insights into your psyche that you wouldn't gain otherwise. One woman who works in a Colorado quilt store told me how when she first started working there she was mainly attracted to traditional flowery fabrics. But then she found herself purchasing batiks and other contemporary fabrics. Perhaps this was her way of breaking out of the mold she had designed for herself. She dressed in a very traditional, matronly manner—a jumper in a light-blue color— wore her hair in a sedate bun, and gave off an air of homespun goodness. But inside, it seems, there was a contemporary quilter itching to break out—which she did with her batiks, putting a new twist into traditionally designed quilts and merging the tradition of quilting with the contemporary edge of the twenty-first century.

Crafts can even provide a psychological boost to your weight-loss efforts. Knitting a sweater, sewing a pillow, repainting a bedroom, or working on a scrapbook can distract you from mindless or emotional eating. And when your hands are sticky with glue or you're working on a delicate fabric, you're less prone to reach for a snack. There is also evidence that by reducing stress, crafts can reduce the production of the stress hormone cortisol, which drives appetite and has been linked to dangerous belly fat. Less stress, less cortisol, less belly fat. It's all good!

Purging September 11, 2001

Each of us coped with the horror of seeing the World Trade Center towers in New York City shatter, collapse, and burn in our own way. For many of us, our crafts were the route to catharsis. "Making a quilt gave me a place to put my feelings about 9/11 so they weren't always with me," says Judy Cohen of Plymouth, Vermont, a former coat designer who worked in New York City for much of her life. "For weeks on end, the image of the buildings coming down in a cloud of smoke and fire was in my head. I couldn't shake it, and at the oddest times, I'd suddenly break down and cry."

A week after the tragedy, Judy was in her sewing room, sorting through her fabrics and preparing to make a quilt unrelated to the attacks. "But I couldn't get the image out of my mind," she recalls. "It was etched into my brain. As I fingered my fabrics, I was drawn to ones that mirrored the colors of that image. I saw that one fabric looked like the flames and another like the meltdown of steel, while another conveyed the fear the people in the building must have felt." Without having a real plan in mind, Judy began putting pieces of fabric up on a design board. Suddenly, she realized she was making a quilt—not of the actual physical scene, but rather an abstract representation of the emotions that were impressed on her mind and body.

As she pieced the quilt together over the next few days, Judy found she often had to leave her sewing room, overcome with emotion, only returning when she felt calmer. But as the scraps of fabric merged into the image in her head, healing emotions began to overtake her fearful, sad feelings, and her crying jags ended. "Making the quilt was a cathartic experience, helping me to work through my feelings about September 11 and commemorate the event," she says. "If I couldn't have made a quilt, I don't know how I would have gotten over this."

Psychological Research Emerges

Since the publication of *Craft to Heal* in 2005, I've heard from several people who are interested in the psychological benefits of crafting and are trying to study it. At the risk of boring you with too much scientific talk, I'll quickly highlight some of the published and unpublished research in bullets.

- Ann Collier, PhD, of the Psychology Department of the University of Wisconsin-Eau Claire, has conducted one survey of how women use textiles to cope with difficult moods in their daily life and is preparing another (to enroll, go to www.uwec. edu/psyc/Who/collier.htm). Dr. Collier electronically surveyed 891 women—and lo and behold, found 47% of the participants use their craft to change a terrible mood. She found that "textile-copers," as she calls them, most often turn to knitting or crocheting when they're upset. Most of the women have tried

11 different crafts and engage in these activities to feel grounded and to cope with life, for intellectual stimulation, and "because of their aesthetic love of textiles"—meaning the tactile pleasure they get from touching yarn and fibers. They also feel that the creative activity is part of their identity and regard it as a crucial form of self-expression.

- Betsan Corkhill of the British organization Stitchlinks is conducting surveys on her website (www.stitchlinks.com) researching the therapeutic benefits of crafting—in particular, knitting and stitching. She and others have found that these crafts distract people from "the relentlessness of long-term pain," if only for a short period of time, which helps to improve their outlook on life, while the rhythmic and repetitive action induces a form of meditation and slows the thought process. Ms. Corkhill says that performing the craft in a group setting also relieves the feelings of social isolation that often increase depression in people with chronic illnesses and pain. "Knitting and stitching can be used in the health arena, workplace, in education and socially, making them powerful tools for improving wellbeing and quality of life for everyone," she says.

- Researchers from Glasgow, Scotland recently published a study of 29 quilters in the *Journal of Public Health* in which the study subjects say that the colored fabrics they use in their quilts give them a psychological lift. They find quilting is a challenging craft, and it gives them the opportunity to learn new skills. It also brings on a sense of complete absorption, boosts their self-esteem, and offers them a strong social network. Finally, giving the quilts away to others as gifts or to those in need adds purpose and meaning to their creative pursuit. All told, these benefits lead the researchers to conclude that "creative craft hobbies such as quilting can be a meaningful vehicle for enhancing wellbeing."

- A couple of English studies focus on women who have been diagnosed with multiple sclerosis (MS), chronic fatigue syndrome, or depression: These women say that crafting helps them cope with their illness and feel more satisfied with life on an everyday basis. Many took up a craft after their illness began because they felt they could engage in the activity despite their ill health and disability. They quickly learned that the craft fills a void in their lives since they can't work anymore and distracts them from thinking about their illness. The study subjects also report that their craft gives them an outlet through which they can express their grief about their health, and it provides them with a social network.

- Michelle Keating, RN, OCN, MSCN, with the John F. Krey Cancer Center in St. Louis, Missouri, and her colleagues are pursuing a study investigating the influence of creative art on self-esteem, hope, and other psychological factors in people with MS. As someone who has MS herself, Ms. Keating firmly believes that creative art has the potential to improve the mental well-being of people with this disabling illness.

- Other published studies focus on people with cancer, and show that crafts and art-making allow them to be more than "just someone with cancer." Crafts allow them to do something meaningful with their lives, provide an avenue for them to relieve negative and fearful feelings about their health, decrease depression and anxiety, and improve their self-esteem.

Thanks to the psychological boost crafts provide, the Society for Arts in Healthcare estimates that over half of the 2,500 hospitals in the United States now have art therapy programs in place for patients of all types—from children and adolescents to adults, from patients with mental illnesses such as depression and schizophrenia, to those with chronic illnesses such as MS, cardiovascular disease, and cancer.

Craft Benefits for the Mentally Ill

Can crafts be formal treatment tools? No doubt. Numerous hospitals across the United States are now utilizing crafts such as knitting, crocheting, and quilting in the treatment, rehabilitation, and recovery of people with mental illnesses. For instance, Ronni Donza, RN, a psychiatric nurse who runs handicraft sessions as part of a Continuing Day Treatment Program for people with schizophrenia and depression at the Richmond University Medical Center on Staten Island, New York, has found that craft activities have profound calming and relaxation benefits for people with mental illness. Performing crafts in a social setting allows clients to interact with others and talk in a nonthreatening but therapeutic environment about their feelings and the challenges they face due to their illness, she says. It also has long-term benefits in that it boosts their self-esteem and gives them the opportunity to contribute to society by donating the things they make—

baby blankets, scarves, hats—to homeless women and children. Finally, "this subtle, pleasurable intervention," as she describes it, reduces the stigma of having a mental illness by leveling the playing field: In the craft room, people who are usually treated as patients can be found helping others work on their projects, and can interact as equals with higher-functioning individuals.

Hey, I Did a Study, Too!

Since I'm obviously a great believer in the stress-reducing effects of crafts and I was finding very little scientific literature to back up my ideas, in 2009 I took it upon myself to perform a small study of crafters. Yes, me! You see, when I'm not writing about creativity, I'm writing about medicine, so I was already versed in the ways of scientific studies and how to design them. (But I also dutifully bought a book on designing psychological studies, too.) The objective of the study was to explore the effects of crafts and hobbies on people's overall well-being and their feelings of sadness and anxiety.

My nephew and I distributed flyers asking for study participants at local craft stores. When that didn't work (it wasn't as easy to get people to sign up as I'd hoped, even with the offer of $50 for their participation), I posted recruitment notices on various craft-oriented websites and sent emails to friends and acquaintances. Eventually, I was able to enroll 11 healthy women between the ages of 37 and 64 who crafted about once a week. I asked each person to take a stress survey before and after they crafted for half an hour for one week. I put two people in a control group, where I asked them not to craft but rather to read a newspaper or news magazine or watch a news show for half an hour a day.

Happily, the results unanimously showed what I know to be true: Everyone found their craft helped them to lower their stress level and to feel better psychologically. Two of the people in the crafting group showed good to excellent benefits on their well-being from performing their craft or hobby and the other seven showed modest benefits. The results were particularly strong for reductions in feeling stressed, feeling sad or blue, and feeling anxious or jittery.

In the news group, one person experienced an increase in her stress level after watching the news, particularly in the evening, and the other showed no change.

This wasn't a rigorously performed scientific study by any means (for one thing, I ended up enrolling dedicated crafters who were already predisposed to agree with my hypothesis that crafts are therapeutic), but it still shows that crafts can be an important part of a stress-reducing regimen. Results from surveys conducted annually by the Craft and Hobby Association also show this to be true: Most crafters say they pursue their craft because it helps them to relax and lower their stress level.

You can try the stress test I gave the subjects in the study yourself. Using the scale on page 47, take the test before and after you engage in your favorite hobby and see if it helps to relax you. If it doesn't, you may be being too perfectionistic about it, or you may want to find another craft that will relax you.

Boosting Your Self-Esteem—and More

Many therapists say that having a craft that allows you to express yourself can be a panacea against wallowing and low self-esteem. Being able to get small things done, like making a notecard

Stress Quiz

Take this survey before and after you start crafting.

On a scale of 1-10 (1 being "not at all" and 10 being "very stressed"), rate how you feel today.

		Not at all			Somewhat						Very
1.	I feel "stressed out."	1	2	3	4	5	6	7	8	9	10
2.	I feel sad or blue.	1	2	3	4	5	6	7	8	9	10
3.	I feel anxious or jittery.	1	2	3	4	5	6	7	8	9	10
4.	I feel tired.	1	2	3	4	5	6	7	8	9	10
5.	I feel hopeless.	1	2	3	4	5	6	7	8	9	10
6.	I feel dissatisfied with my life.	1	2	3	4	5	6	7	8	9	10
7.	I feel worthless or like a failure.	1	2	3	4	5	6	7	8	9	10
8.	I feel irritable.	1	2	3	4	5	6	7	8	9	10
9.	I feel angry.	1	2	3	4	5	6	7	8	9	10
10.	I feel like crying.	1	2	3	4	5	6	7	8	9	10
11.	I don't have much appetite.	1	2	3	4	5	6	7	8	9	10
12.	I overeat because I'm feeling anxious or bored.	1	2	3	4	5	6	7	8	9	10
13.	I have a lot of aches and pains.	1	2	3	4	5	6	7	8	9	10
14.	I don't have an interest in my usual activities or people.	1	2	3	4	5	6	7	8	9	10
15.	I am having more trouble than usual making decisions or concentrating.	1	2	3	4	5	6	7	8	9	10

In general, how do you feel right now?

_____

_____

_____

_____

_____

_____

_____

or sewing a sleeve on a garment, may be just what you need to give yourself a feeling of "self-efficacy," and keep your mood humming along, or boost it on bad days. There's even strong psychological evidence that journal writing and crafts that allow you to vent your emotions and release them physically can move you forward in your journey toward growth and healing, says career coach and writer Gail McMeekin.

"Any creative activity offers us valuable personal insights," says McMeekin. "For me, painting and writing are both emotional releases that allow me to express repressed or difficult feelings. They also give me a different slant on a topic. For example, if I am writing and get stuck on a chapter, I might paint a picture of it and see what I can garner from it."

Likewise, Anne-Marie Burke, an interior designer in Massachusetts, creates mixed-media collage memorials as a way of grieving for friends and family she's lost. "I don't often give myself permission to cry," Anne-Marie says, "so I think these memorials are my way of releasing tears. They help me get out my feelings about the person and the loss I feel so I can move on with my life."

"If we don't allow our bodies to rest from the pressures of everyday life, we are placing ourselves at risk for heart disease or other illnesses. Creative activities and hobbies—like sewing—can help a person focus on something productive and get away from their worries for a while."

—Robert H. Reiner, PhD

For Giovonnia Vaughan, an administrative assistant for the New York City Fire Department, crafting has played a "huge role" in her recovery from depression. "When I was sad, I would pick up my knitting needles and head for Central Park. I spent hours under a tree with my yarn and needles. Whenever things seemed too chaotic for me, knitting helped me to make order out of something," she explains. "Or I would design a quilt out of whatever I was feeling that day. I would use blues and browns for sadness, and yellows and reds for happiness. Often I didn't use a pattern; I just followed whatever I was feeling. I felt I was giving life to whatever was going on inside of me. It helped me have a sense of accomplishment when I felt I couldn't do anything right." And after September 11, knitting and sewing gave Giovonnia a place to feel safe when the New York City around her felt wildly unsafe.

The stories about the mental benefits of crafts are all around us. You've probably heard a few of your own. Every time I've talked with others about this topic, the stories and enthusiasm spill out, for we can all feel, without being told, that doing what you love brings a feeling of well-being and rejuvenation. Unleashing your creative energies reveals undiscovered or repressed sides of yourself, and helps you weather life's ups and downs. In short, crafts provide a warm and fuzzy place to be yourself and feel safe, a port from the storm, even (or especially) when the world around you is falling apart.

Beyond Art Therapy

In the beginning, there was art therapy. Along with dance, music, poetry, writing, and drama therapies, the process of making art has been used for years to reach those who can't articulate what they're feeling—from autistic and abused children to the mentally disturbed. More recently, expressive art therapy has emerged. Whereas traditional art therapy focuses on the product and an art therapist's interpretation of that product, expressive art therapy targets the process of creating art as a cathartic and healing experience, and on the interpretation of the product by the creator, not the therapist (the thinking being that while others may express opinions about your art, only you can know what your creation truly and personally says). Today, it has been established that the expressive art therapy process also has benefits for psychologically healthy people, helping them to achieve their potential as individuals, to grow and change, and to live life to the fullest.

Expressive art therapists believe that negative thoughts and painful or fearful feelings take up actual physical residence in the body. Traditionally, talk therapy—psychotherapy—has been used to release and resolve such feelings, but simply talking about your feelings may not release them, and may actually lead you to relive them. "Griping and moaning about your feelings won't make you feel better," says expressive art therapist

Barbara Ganim. "It just reactivates the stress response." A more effective way to approach their release may be through expressive art therapy. Because imagery is the inner language of the mind-body—it reacts to images of a thought before it recognizes the words that describe that thought, according to the split-brain research of Dr. Roger Sperry—drawing and visually expressing what you are feeling is often cathartic in a way that just talking isn't.

In working with cancer patients for the past decade, Ganim has found that "as soon as a patient expresses a painful emotion through color, shape, and form, it energetically releases blocked energy and stops the stress response. Art moves stress-producing emotions and blockages out of the body using the body's own language of imagery," she says.

The Expressive Art Process

In her book *Visual Journaling: Going Deeper than Words*, Ganim describes a process she has developed for helping patients go deeper with their creative work, to tap into the healing benefits. Here's the technique in brief:

Step 1

Set an intention. "Real healing comes through intention and expression," says Ganim. "While a mindless activity such as knitting can create a relaxing and meditative state, its effects are only temporary." To truly access your body's deeper innate ability to both heal itself and even prevent illness and stabilize itself, you have to approach your craft with a mission. Your intention can take any number of forms … you might wish to gain insight into why the prospect of seeing your family makes you feel anxious, release anger against your boss, examine the knot of tension in your head that is causing pain, or heal a chronic physical illness such as arthritis. Try to be very specific in your intention.

Step 2

Quiet your mind. To access your feelings and their associated images, to quiet the left brain and give the right brain wider reign, Ganim says you need to disconnect from the distracting thoughts in your mind. You do this by sitting in a comfortable position in a quiet room, closing your eyes, and breathing deeply and slowly. Focus on your breath, the exhale and the inhale. Now, breathing normally, allow your attention to drift to any part of your body where you're feeling tension, discomfort, or pain, and focus on the sensation you feel there.

Step 3

Keeping your eyes closed, imagine what the sensation (or feeling) you've identified in your body would look like if it were an image. What colors, shapes, and forms would that sensation have? The image might be realistic—a mountain, a house, a chair—or abstract, such as a series of squiggly lines. Only you need to know what the image is meant to convey.

Step 4

Create your image. Open your eyes and draw your image with any medium you like—colored pencils, paints, or pastels, or even create a free-form image on the sewing machine.

Step 5

Transform the negative image into a positive image—one that takes your stress-producing emotion and represents it in a more constructive way of reacting to the situation or issue causing you distress. This is the true key to healing with expressive arts and crafts of any kind, says Ganim. "Transformation occurs when you replace an image representing a negative thought or an angry or destructive emotion with a new image that is positive, peaceful, and loving," she explains, "which releases its psychological hold on you." When you change the image in your mind, your body and your spirit respond in kind. She calls this "re-envisioning." The specific technique involves looking at a work you've made about a stressful emotion, having a dialogue with it about what it is saying, and trying to get a new, more positive perspective on it by imagining how the image needs to be changed so that it feels less stressful, and then drawing or painting over the old, negative image or making a new piece of artwork that feels more positive.

Healing Lesson

Crafts can help relieve mental stress,
induce relaxation, boost your mood,
and help you discover as-yet unknown
facets of your personality, serving as a
potent form of self-help therapy. Research
shows that as a visual art form, crafts
communicate in the body's internal
language of images. By crafting with
intention and focus, you can re-envision
negative images as more positive,
constructive images, and release yourself
from stress-producing feelings.

The Physical Benefits of Crafting

6

Recent years have brought major changes in the understanding of the connections between the mind and the body, and the role that leisure pursuits can play in improving health and well-being. What's become clear is that crafts are among the activities that can be used to reduce psychological stress (as I discussed in the last chapter). Now, however, it also appears they can impact physical stress. By helping us access and release negative emotions locked deep inside—emotions that can hamper the immune system and impair the body's normal functioning—art forms may be able to fix some of the physical damage wrought by everyday life and past traumatic experiences.

Mind-Body Healing

Some experts believe that most health problems have a psychosomatic component to them, with negative emotions contributing if not to the cause of illnesses and their symptoms, then to their exacerbation. Over the past fifty years, research in the field of psychoneuroimmunology—an area of medicine that focuses on the effects of different interventions on the mind, brain transmitters, nerves, and the immune system—has shown that creative endeavors can impact this process. According to Michael Samuels, MD, and Mary Rockwood Lane, RN, MSN, authors of

Creative Healing: How to Heal Yourself by Tapping Your Hidden Creativity, when you perform a creative act, your body produces a nerve impulse, hormone, or brain chemical that sends a message out to the body's cells. These cells then spring into action, mounting a defense against invading viruses or cancer cells, or simply just relaxing or tensing the body's muscles and nervous system. "When a person makes art or music, or dances, or pictures an image that is freeing and joyful, the body actually changes its physiology to heal itself," say these authors.

"Art frees your spirit so your mind and body are in harmony. Art frees your immune system to work at its optimum and help you heal. Art helps you conquer disease by freeing your inner healer to work at its optimum."

—Michael Samuels, MD, and Mary Rockwood Lane, RN, MSN, Creative Healing

---

Medical research is beginning to bear the fruits of creative pursuits on the body. For instance, published studies suggest that engaging in cultural, intellectual, and recreational activities, such as ballroom dancing, playing a musical instrument, reading a book, gardening, knitting, or working a crossword puzzle, can slow or prevent memory loss and delay dementia. Another study of asthma and rheumatoid arthritis patients published in the *Journal of the American Medical Association* reports that those who keep diaries— writing about stressful experiences—have fewer symptoms than those who write about neutral topics. Yet another journaling study conducted at North Carolina State University reveals that writing down your feelings about bad or traumatic events helps to improve your memory and concentration—perhaps because placing pen to paper provides a conduit out of the body, so you're released from the memories. Likewise, research involving people in rehabilitation programs demonstrates that those who participate in arts and crafts often do better physically than those who don't—in fact, they may regain their function faster and need less pain medication. And Dr. Herbert Benson at Harvard University has shown that repetitive activity—which he says can include crafts such as knitting and sewing—relieves emotional and physical stress, reversing the stress response and its attendant release of the body-damaging hormones cortisol and adrenaline, and inducing its opposite, the relaxation response.

Creativity Cracks the Aging Code

In addition to protecting the memory, research suggests that crafts and hobbies can stave off the ill effects of aging, helping older adults to retain their function, independence, and quality of life for a longer time than they normally would. What's been learned so far: We need the charge of doing something creative to feel good mentally, particularly as the decades pass. According to neuroscientist Gregory Berns, MD, PhD, author of *Satisfaction: The Science of Finding True Fulfillment*, that's because the level of the brain chemical dopamine, which brings on a natural high, declines as we age. By creating through crafts and seeking out new experiences and learning new skills, however, we can trigger dopamine surges and regain that feeling of satisfaction. George Washington University psychiatrist Gene Cohen, MD, author of *The Mature Mind: The Positive Power of the Aging Brain* and an expert on the health benefits of creativity for older adults, says that trying new things and being creative also promotes brain plasticity (flexibility and growth) and even prompts our brains to rewire, which may fend off dementia and help to maintain health. "When you challenge the brain, your brain cells sprout new connections, called dendrites," he explains, "and new contact points, called synapses, that improve brain communication."

Dr. Cohen has the data to prove that creativity has a powerful anti-aging effect on the mind and body: In a two-year study of healthy older adults (over the age of 65) sponsored by the National Endowment for the Arts, he found that those who engage in painting, writing, poetry, jewelry-making, or singing in a chorale have better overall physical health, make fewer visits to the doctor, use less medication, and have fewer health problems than people who don't participate in cultural programs. The "artsy" group also has better morale and reports less loneliness thanks to feelings of self-control and mastery, and from maintaining their social engagements. "This study proves that you can't have a real health promotion program for the elderly without an art component," he says.

Another benefit of creative activities: They're sustainable. "Art has been in the soul of the species since [the time of] cave people, and its benefits make us keep coming back to it," Dr. Cohen notes. So while you may not stick to an exercise program, you may stick to an art program—which will not only give you a psychological boost, but also a brain boost.

Harvard's George Valliant, MD, who followed 824 people from their teens to old age for over 50 years, found that creativity is one of the pursuits that makes retirement rewarding and satisfying. Likewise, another famous aging study started by Dr. Lawrence

Terman that began in 1921 and followed 1,500 men and women from childhood to adulthood—in some cases for eight decades—found that joining social groups and engaging in hobbies was a key ingredient of longevity.

Basically, these studies show that the happier and more engaged we are in life and with other people, the longer and better we'll live.

The "If Not Now, When?" Phenomenon

Dr. Cohen says that as we enter our 40s and 50s, our brains start firing on all cylinders. We begin using both sides of our brain more (the logical and analytical left side and the artistic right side), which stimulates us to be more creative—while being more creative prompts us to integrate both left- and right-brain capabilities in a happy cycle of artistic energy. As an added bonus, we become more confident and comfortable with ourselves as we age, and so we may cast off the need to conform: After 40, we want to showcase our true selves through the way we speak, act, dress, and the things we do. And we may shed the "should have" way of living we previously endorsed, embracing instead the life we really want to live.

> "Art and healing together are the art of the future and the medicine of the future."
>
> —Michael Samuels, MD, and Mary Rockwood Lane, RN, MSN

"There is a lovely interlude in middle age, when we haven't lost the mental nimbleness of youth and yet we've gained wisdom," says Sue Shellenbarger, author of *The Breaking Point: How Female Midlife Crisis Is Transforming Today's Women.* This is when creativity can blossom with age, she notes, and become a means for validating who we are now.

Dr. Cohen agrees that many people in mid- to late-life go through a psychological "liberation" phase characterized by an increasing urge and feeling of freedom to do the things they've always wanted to do. They hear an inner voice that asks them "If not now, when?" and "Why not—what can they do to me?" that gives them the courage and confidence to try something new and self-expressive.

Perhaps that's why it seems creativity often peaks and our need to create soars later in life: Artist Georgia O'Keefe, for instance, did some of her best work in her later years, and Grandma Moses didn't start painting until she was in her seventies. Likewise, Laura Ingalls Wilder was in her sixties when she began to write her now-classic *Little House on the Prairie* books.

Memory-making Through Scrapbooking

When a loved one becomes chronically ill, there may be a feeling that the opportunities for making wonderful new memories with that person are now gone, erased by the overwhelming responsibilities of caregiving. But the truth is that even though a care recipient is suffering from dementia, recovering from a stroke, bed-bound, or in a wheelchair, the time you share together can still be a time to remember. The key is to find a mutually engrossing and enjoyable activity—and the popular craft of scrapbooking fits the bill nicely.

One of the big psychological pluses associated with

scrapbooking—In fact with any craft or hobby—is that it has the ability to transport both you and your care recipient to a different place, away from routine concerns. "Scrapbooking provides a respite from illness for both the caregiver and the care receiver," concurs Amy Cotton, MSN, APRN, a geriatric nurse practitioner who often provides home care to elderly patients in Bangor, Maine. "You're connecting with one another rather than just dealing with the illness or visiting, so scrapbooking can be a very positive, relationship-building tool."

Scrapbooking also allows you to view the person you're caring for in a new way: By hearing the stories behind the pictures and mementoes you comb through as you craft, you have the opportunity to see your loved one not as the physically frail person he or she has become, but as the vibrant person he once was. That was true for television celebrity Leeza Gibbons. She started scrapbooking as a way to bridge the communication gap with her mother, Jean, after she was diagnosed with Alzheimer's disease. "When my mom's cognitive ability began to slip away it was in small, manageable pieces in the beginning," she writes on her website (www.leezagibbons.com). "We would sit for hours and pour through her memory boxes and photos getting girlishly giddy over tickets to a dance with a young boyfriend, and misty-eyed at the sight of her firstborn, my brother. She couldn't quite remember which of the three kids it was, but love is love and once you've felt it and given it away, that never leaves you."

Finally, making an album of your past creates a beautiful keepsake for future generations, explains Bernie Siegel, MD, author of *101 Exercises for the Soul: A Divine Workout for Body, Mind, and Spirit,* and offers the chance to take stock, a process that can be both emotional and insightful. "Memories are how we pass down our traditions and preserve our legacies," notes Gibbons. "It's what resonates at the end of the day and at the end of a life. Memories matter."

The Meaning of Craft Studies

Despite the emerging studies on the topic, some scientists will tell you that the evidence to support the ability of crafts to physically heal is anecdotal—based mostly on people's stories rather than rigorous scientific studies. A valid criticism. But what matters is not whether crafts really do offer healing benefits, but that we believe they do. No one is saying that crafts and art can cure cancer or other diseases, but there is no question that they can be used in a complementary manner to bolster the effects of traditional medicine. And they can heal the soul—allowing people to find peace and a sense of wholeness, even if their illnesses of the body can't be cured. At the very least, crafts can help individuals release some of their fear and find joy in the present moment, no matter what their physical circumstances.

Evidence or not, people have been using their crafts to maintain and restore functionality after illness or surgery—and they've often confounded (and convinced) doctors of the healing powers of crafts in the process. Anne Morgan Jefferson of Hampton Falls, New

Hampshire, for example, used knitting as a form of rehabilitation for her hand and arm after she lost her left elbow to a rare bone infection. "Even though it was painful, I figured out a way to brace my arm on couch pillows so I could knit for two to three hours a day," she says. "No one told me to do it, but I knew it was therapeutic for me—and because of it, I can still use my left hand. My hand surgeon was astounded, considering all I'd been through."

Likewise, Margo Martin, a lifelong sewer living in Houston, Texas, used her craft in her recovery from brain surgery. Despite being told that it might take as long as nine months for her sight to return to normal after an operation to remove two benign tumors, Margo tried sewing as soon as she could. Within two weeks of the surgery, she was sewing—and seeing better—again. And she's sure that her love of her craft and her eagerness to get back to it played a role.

For Cynthia Birrer, a former child psychology educator at the University of Witwatersrand in Johannesburg, South Africa, putting hand to cloth helped to retrain her brain. In 1975, she was diagnosed with the degenerative nerve disease multiple sclerosis (MS). In 1981, bed-bound with a dismal prognosis and unable to resume her career, Cynthia's husband, Bill, suggested that she try sewing on a machine for her enjoyment, something she had once done with enthusiasm. She went to work on the machine, reluctantly, because she resented being reduced to "woman's work" after once having had a thriving career as an academic. The effort was exhausting: Her fingers had curled under the palms and it was difficult for her to control the movement of the fabric under the presser foot. But she kept at it, and a year later she was proficient enough to make a series of machine-embroidered pictures, which eventually were published as a children's picturebook. Over the next few years, Cynthia completed several more picturebooks, working eight hours a day, seven days a week to meet her book deadlines. Gradually, she became aware that as her sewing skills improved, her MS improved. In fact, by the end of the 1980s, her MS had gone into remission to such an extent that "neurologists who did not know my history could find no trace of the disease," she recalls.

Cynthia believes that the use of her hands helped to reconfigure and heal her brain and nervous system. "I was aware at the time that the rhythm imposed by the up-down thrust of the needle was affecting my hand movements," she says. "My hands began to move in sync and I regained full control." In the years since her recovery, she has devoted herself to educating others about the role of crafts in healing. "Work which demands the skilled use of the hands affords the brain new ways of approaching old tasks, as well as the possibility of undertaking and mastering new tasks," she says on her CD, *The Knowing Hand*. "The brain can be educated and reeducated."

"I swear by crafts as a powerful antidote for disability and for recovery," agrees Colleen Kelly Spengler, an Illinois woman who has often been bedridden due to illness. "The emotional well-being you get from creative projects just cannot be understood until you need something like that in your life. Injuries and ill health make you feel helpless, and being creative is the opposite of that: you prove to yourself that whatever you can imagine can be achieved, or at least attempted. That attitude has served me well in my search for better health."

These stories highlight that despite all odds, healing can occur just by virtue of a little "handiwork." The women here knew that their love for crafting would offer them pleasure and fulfillment as they recovered from illness—and maybe they even knew it would help them physically. For them, crafts gave hope and healing.

Healing Lesson

Crafts and other art forms may have the ability to create actual physiologic changes in the body, serving as rehabilitative therapy after injury, surgery, or illness, boosting the immune system, and staving off the aging process.

The Spiritual Benefits of Crafting

7

To me, to find your spirit and your spirituality means to live authentically, to be the person you were meant to be, to find your place in the universe and in the scheme of things. Like meditation and prayer, crafts can bring you to a quiet place, another dimension, where you can get in touch with this authentic self and connect with your spirit.

"Sometimes, creativity is a route to corners of the soul we didn't know existed."

—Alice Domar, PhD, Self-Nurture

"I find that daily life pulls me away from the spiritual, and my craft draws me back to it. It gives me an incredible feeling of peace," says Jana Clover, a divorced mother of four who owns a stained-glass shop in Auburn, California. Giovonnia Vaughan of New York City says that her knitting is a form of prayer. "I love to find a quiet spot and sit in the silence, knit, and talk to God. In each stitch, there is a prayer and a blessing, and I center myself with the world." She adds, "I cannot imagine my life without my craft work."

Julia Cameron, author of *The Artist's Way: A Spiritual Path to Higher Creativity*, makes no distinction between creativity and spirituality: to her, getting in touch with your creativity also puts you in touch with your spirit, and getting in touch with your spirit puts you in touch with your creativity. "We speak of the Creator, but we seldom see that word as another word for 'artist,'" she notes. "And yet, clearly, a great artist made the world. We, in turn, are creations of this Creator, and are meant to continue its creativity by being creative ourselves. It might be said that the act of making art is actually a form of prayer. Similarly, when people take time for prayer, their deepened spirituality urges them to create."

> "Creativity is God's gift to us. Using our creativity is our gift back to God."
>
> —Julia Cameron, The Artist's Way

Coach and author Gail McMeekin agrees, noting that "Creativity is a very spiritual process because it comes from our uniqueness as individuals. It comes from our soul center and expresses who we are and what we see and believe."

Crafts Can Be Good Spiritual Medicine

In the crafter's cult classic, *The Knitting Sutra*, Susan Gordon Lydon uses knitting as a way to rehabilitate a broken bone in her right arm and discovers en route that the craft is more than just a way of exercising her hands, as her doctor advises her to do, or simply a route to creative expression. For her, it is a meditative experience and a way to discover the "stillness within, a way to contact the soul." She finds that the lessons of knitting—being still, focusing the mind, asking for help—can and should be applied to everyday life, because they bring us closer to serenity and insight.

Lydon is talking about something that doctors are now recognizing: that prayer, and by extension, crafts such as knitting, can be as good for your health as meditation and deep breathing. Some three hundred scientific studies show that having a strong spiritual connection can lead to lower stress levels, less depression and anxiety, and a greater sense of purpose and meaning in life. And, for reasons as yet unknown, those who have a strong spiritual conviction suffer fewer signs and symptoms of mental and physical problems and go to the doctor less often than others. Yet you needn't go to church to be spiritual or religious. You need only believe in a higher power at work in the universe, be it God, Goddess, Mother Nature, energy (since our bodies themselves are simple energy), or a force greater than yourself.

For Becci Fairchild of Bullhead, Arizona, who has cancer, finding quilting over the past couple of years has helped her to push away the physical pain she is feeling and helped her talk to God. "I use quilting for pain management, and most of the time it works because my mind steps away from the frailty of the human body," she explains. "I get lost in the colors, the feel of the fabric, and the design in my mind." Through her quilts she hopes to show her grandson and great-nephew that imagination has no limits, that there is joy in self-expression, that it is important to try even when the goal seems impossible to reach, that you must have the courage to face anything that life hands you, and that you should live your life so that at the end you can say you have no regrets. "As I have grown sicker with each year, I have struggled with the spiritual side of my life," says Becci. "But when I'm working on a project, I have time to really talk to God, and more importantly, to listen. When I am working on something, I get so

> "The painting has a life of its own. I try to let it come through."
>
> —Jackson Pollock

69

lost in it that I actually think sometimes that I'm having an out-of-body experience. And when I come back to earth, I'm always amazed at what has been created in the absence of my ego. How could I not know that this is a miracle?" This experience makes Becci look at everyone and everything just a little bit differently. "When I am working on a quilt, I have a peace that I have never known before. The end product is always a sweet reward, but it is the journey there that I find spiritual. I have learned so much about myself and this wonderful world through the creative process."

Julia Cameron says that making art is a "spiritual transaction" and an act of faith, for crafts and creativity are gifts of the spirit. They add beauty to the world. And perhaps that is a crafter's mission: to bring beauty to everyday life, and, in return, to find peace and healing.

Healing Lesson

Crafts can help you reconnect with your authentic self, your core beliefs and values, and your higher power. As gifts of the spirit and to the spirit, they bring beauty to the world.

Part II

How to Reap the Healing Benefits of Crafts

Find a Craft You Love 8

Things you love create immediate psychological and physiological responses. Seeing your child or pet fills you with happiness. Coming home after a trip makes you feel safe. Pictures spark happy memories that literally warm you. And working at a favorite hobby makes you feel great, not only while you're doing it, but often when you're just thinking about it.

The trick is to find a craft you truly love so you can access its benefits. Not all crafts appeal to everyone. And some people even have a problem with the word "crafts," conjuring up images of Popsicle sticks, pipe cleaners, and tissue holders made from plastic and yarn, or what educators call "trash crafts," says San Francisco psychotherapist Virginia Baille. They fail to see that crafts can actually refer to sophisticated jewelry, furniture, textiles, and true art.

> "Only when people are in touch with their passions do they use their heads to give shape and substance to their dreams."
>
> —Richard Chang, The Passion Plan

So how do you find your passion? Before you plunge in and spend a bundle on craft supplies you might never use, consider these thoughts, courtesy of freelance creative writer and independent filmmaker Linda J. Peckel...

Mapping Your Craft Style

By Linda J. Peckel

(Blog: http://artsenclave.wordpress.com)

We all have a personality style—and a creative style—that dictates the types of crafts we'll like. Several of my friends indulge in crafts that I consider to be excruciating, and few of them can appreciate what I find so relaxing about the many long laborious home decorating projects I undertake. The only thing I find relaxing about quilting, for example, is watching my sister do it and then hanging the result on my wall. And my friend who loves to bake gives so much attention to each detail that I find I've wandered from the kitchen to watch Oprah while she's still mixing the dough. (My cakes have yet to turn out right, unless of course I have the assistance of Betty Crocker.) In these cases, it's not the process, but the precision that I find unappealing. With my very general approach to life and art, I find both of these crafts are better left to others with the patience for them.

Because of this, it occurred to me that not everyone is suited to every kind of craft. While this observation definitely doesn't qualify me for the space program, it's a surprisingly overlooked conclusion: just because you *can* do something doesn't mean you *should*. (Let's call this Rule No. 1.) I'm sure I could master the complexities of knitting a sweater or building a log cabin from a kit from Sears, but would the stress involved be worth it? And after a weekend of helping me slide sticky wallpaper around walls that may have been constructed in Pisa, my friend (the interior designer) informed me that she was not enjoying the process as much as I was. I called it creative. She called it work. I had a sense of satisfaction. She had a sense of exhaustion and mild annoyance. That's when I learned Rule No. 2: when craft becomes an obligation, it's no longer fun.

Craft Mirrors Personality

There's no doubt about it, personality plays a big part in recreation. What relaxes one mind is likely to be perceived as labyrinthine torture by another. But how can you know what you will like before you try it? The answer to this question could save us all a lot of hours, days, or whole weekends committed to misery over a potter's wheel, a lathe, a loom, in the kitchen, or at the center of a quilting circle.

For the last century, psychologists have been examining just how particular personality traits express themselves, and they've been able to identify a large number of significant patterns. In fact, most psychologists divide the general population into four basic types, although the names of these types and their definitions vary. The Williams Scale, for instance, measures four levels of creative thinking: curiosity, imagination, complexity, and risk-taking, while the Keirsey Temperament Sorter categorizes people as either rationals, idealists, artisans, or guardians, and the Briggs-Meyers Personality Type Assessment classifies people as extraverts or introverts, sensors or intuitives, thinkers or feelers, and judgers or perceivers. I simply took a few of these patterns and applied them to crafting. Here are three basic distinctions that might clue you in to what will soothe your spirit:

1. Disciplined Creative vs. Spontaneous Creative

The first thing you need to know about yourself is whether you like to live by the rules or leave them behind. Another way to look at this is to ask yourself whether you like to make order out of chaos or pull chaos out of order. A disciplined creative likes to put order in the universe, and starting with something as small as a sweater is reassuring. They start with a plan, pattern, or recipe for the project they are undertaking, acquire the materials and supplies they will need to execute it, and even schedule the time and place to do the crafting. There is a neat predictable beginning, middle, and end (which for these dedicated types often results in a Christmas or birthday gift for some lucky relative). Quilting is a good example of a disciplined craft, where the many steps involved in searching for fabrics, thinking of a pattern, and organizing and executing a complete quilt from what used to be a lot of scraps offers a sense of restoring order to a scattered world. Other disciplined creatives work in very technical detail-oriented kinds of crafts, like beadwork, lace making, crewel/embroidery, and baking.

Those who favor the other side of the street like to see how far they can bend the rules. They often decide about fifteen minutes before they sit down that they are "in the mood" to craft. It's not that these people don't plan, because certainly they learn— at least over time—to keep around the materials they will need to do something, should the creative spark ignite. But they don't plan when or what they are going to do, they often don't worry about whether it will ever be completed, and they don't necessarily have any notion of what the end result will be, but let the project evolve on its own. These are people who let their tears spill over the potter's wheel at midnight or get the urge to scrapbook at 7:30 on a Friday night and work through the night to complete it (but may never finish the last page). The craft is the thing. It's a Zen experience and a very satisfying one.

2. Detail-Minded vs. General-Minded

Here's another of those hairs to split that can really make the difference between crafting agony and ecstasy: whether you have a mind that focuses on details or on generalities. The wrong choice can push you over the edge and leave you more stressed out than when you started. Detail-oriented people will naturally focus exclusively on a single task at a time, like crocheting a baby afghan, decoupaging a jewelry box, or making a mosaic end table. The repetition of the same elements over and over again calms the mind, while the gradual accumulation of great skill at a single task provides satisfaction.

At the opposite end of the same spectrum are the generalists—the impressionists of crafting, whose works need to be viewed from afar to make sense of them. These are the people who (again like me) are unfazed by small imperfections because their minds are constantly focused on the big picture. To them, detail work—like needlepoint, beadwork, and even the measuring involved in baking a cake—is tedious to the point of being painful. As a generalist, I use words like "plotz," "schlop," and "squeeze" to describe my application of wallpaper and/or paint. I am anything but exact, which is why I choose crafts that end up looking good without great attention to detail, like gardening. Generalists draw their relaxation from constantly focusing on what the project needs next, and they like to juggle multiple priorities.

Martha Stewart shows signs of being a classic generalist. She knows a billion and a half little facts about six hundred thousand crafts (who but her knew there were so many?), but you rarely see her do the same thing twice. That's because the satisfaction from this kind of crafting comes from adding yet another skill set to your ever-growing basket. And once you've done something, you don't need to do it again. (Next time I'll hire someone to do the wallpaper, as the thrill will be gone—I'm off to tile the backsplash now.)

3. Collaborator vs. Rugged Individualist

This is where we see the impact of classic extraverted/introverted personality traits. Certain kinds of crafts call for the work of two or more people, due to the amount of lifting or the need for extra hands. This includes some kinds of jewelry making, glass blowing, furniture making, home decorating, and gardening/landscaping. Other crafts, such as quilting, knitting, rubber stamping, cooking, fabric dying, egg decorating, and scrapbooking, lend themselves to socializing, but don't require it. This social aspect adds to the enjoyment of the craft and increases your knowledge base as you share your experiences. And the bonus is that you can finally collect your due honors for a finished piece from your esteemed peers, which is about a hundred times more satisfying than the "oh, that's nice" comments from your family and friends.

At the far end of this scale are the "rugged individualists," the mountaineers of crafters. These are the whittlers, the painters, and the poets among us. They go to the woods to get away from the rest of the world. They use their crafts to regain their sanity after a day surrounded by those they love and especially those they don't. While most people aren't quite this extreme, everyone needs time to celebrate themselves, to be alone and comfortable in their own skin. Crafts are extensions of your personality, your needs, your creativity, and sometimes that's just for you. At these quiet times, you may do the same thing that you also share with others, like quilting or knitting, or you may slip away to your garden, studio, or back room to shut the world out for just a little while and reclaim your spirit.

> "When I stand before God at the end of my life, I would hope that I would not have a single bit of talent left, and could say 'I used everything you gave me.'"
>
> —Erma Bombeck

Making Your Choice

Ultimately, it's important to recognize that no one craft is all one thing or another. Beadwork can be detail-oriented, but it can be done in a solitary or social setting. Certain kinds of weaving, woodcrafts requiring assembly, home decorating projects, landscaping (as opposed to simple gardening), and even cooking may require the collaborative effort of two or more people, and they can be both disciplined and spontaneous. You were probably able to identify the leanings of your personality as you read through this essay, but you may still be wondering what that means about the crafts you should pursue. That brings us to Rule No. 3 in crafts (and life): do what appeals to *you*, and if you don't like it, *stop*. Nobody says you have to finish a quilt, a sweater, or a cake. And if you start painting the walls and don't like the effect, talk your spouse, sibling, son, or daughter into finishing the job, or save your pennies and hire a handyman. Crafts are not meant to be taken too seriously—that's what the rest of life is for.

Healing Lesson

Not all crafts appeal to all crafters, and
finding the right craft has as much to do
with matching your personality traits as
your brain style.

Make Time and Space for Your Craft

9

It's time to reframe your craft time in your mind: think of it no longer as a self-indulgence, but rather as a medical necessity. Dr. Herbert Benson of Harvard University advises performing the relaxation response or meditation daily for at least twenty minutes—so the same holds true if you're performing a craft. "View your craft as if it were a medication that you need to take every day for optimal benefit," says New York University psychologist Robert Reiner, PhD. "If you stop taking the drug or doing the craft, you'll lose the benefit."

Coach Gail McMeekin admits that carving out craft time can be a tough task, especially for women. "But even if it's difficult to schedule, it's important to make time for crafts because they allow you to tune into your body and your creativity, to release frustration and tap into your deepest emotions," she says.

"If it is woman's function to give, she must be replenished too."

—Anne Morrow Lindbergh, Gift from the Sea

"Time is a challenge for all of us, but those who express themselves creatively give themselves permission to do so," continues McMeekin. Diane Ericson, a fabric artist and pattern designer, advises crafters to "Stop waiting for the perfect situation—when the kids are in school, when you're alone on a weekend—and for others to give you their permission or approval. Making time for the creative process is making time for you." She also notes that you indirectly mentor your children when you show them that you value yourself enough to make time for yourself. Give the kids something to do for a half hour and tell them that you'll be over in your crafting space doing your own thing. If you nurture yourself, you'll have more to give to your family. And you'll be making a statement to yourself about your value. "Most women don't make time for themselves. Instead, they're off cleaning the bathroom floor—which gives them the message that the floor is more important than they are," she says.

Marcy Tilton, Ericson's partner and a fabric artist in her own right, recommends making a commitment to daily creativity practice. "It will help you because it feels good while you're doing it, but also, like exercise, the benefits will stay with you throughout the day."

Claiming a Crafting Space

Having a room of one's own, to borrow from Virginia Woolf, is important for all humans. The room needn't be large, but McMeekin suggests setting up a dedicated craft space in your home—rather than occasionally commandeering the dining room table—so you can play whenever you have a few moments to spare. Since I work at home, I often take a "craft break" during the day to sit at my sewing machine and sew a few quilt blocks together. This break may not last more than ten minutes, but I always arise from my sewing chair happier than when I first sat down, feeling like I've made progress on a project. It also takes me out of the left-brain work space I've been in (since I write mostly about health and nutrition topics) and puts me in a soothing right-brain space. It makes me feel creative even when I'm dealing with numbers, charts, and facts, rather than flights of fancy.

Ericson says to look at your current storage areas to see if any have the potential to become a craft room. "You might find that if you clear that space out, you'll have your craft area. I have one student who created a space in the little nook underneath the basement stairs. She painted the walls and put a little table and chair in there, along with some material and a notebook."

In short, seek and ye shall find, whether it's just a basket or a corner of the kitchen. "Put your craft supplies in the car or take over part of a room or office," advises McMeekin. "Just find a space that is yours alone."

Healing Lesson

It's important to make time and a place for your crafts. This is easier said than done, but remember: your needs are as important as everyone else's, and you need to do this for you. So give yourself permission—and do it!

Build a Social
Network of Crafters 10

Aging studies tell us that life-long learning and having a strong social network are two of the keys to a healthy and happy retirement. Taking a craft class qualifies on both scores, helping you to advance your skills and introducing you to other crafters. "Countless studies show that socializing with others is an effective way to release stress," says Dr. Robert Reiner of New York University. "Human beings are social animals. We need to interact with other people to stay healthy."

Besides finding others with like-minded interests, classes are critical for locating a mentor who can offer guidance when you need it. "Just make sure your mentor allows you to express yourself, rather than dictating that you do things her way," advises creativity coach Gail McMeekin. "You want to release your creativity, not squash it." Quilting teacher Ricky Tims, of Arvada, Colorado, tries to give his students the tools and encouragement to make the quilts that are dancing in *their* heads. "I don't want my students to make Ricky Tims quilts," he says. "I want them to make their own, to create their own visions."

"Having a creative network is incredibly important," explains fabric artist and teacher Diane Ericson. "Women, in particular, need to be connected to others. But this network should mirror what's important to you." To form your own creativity network, take a risk and invite other crafters you've met (say at retreats or in your guild) who share your interests to keep in touch and get

"Perhaps within each
of us there is a need
to stretch. Perhaps
within each of us
there is a daring
spirit that whispers to
be heard."

—Sue Bender,
Stretching Lessons

together for design play, challenges, knitting circles, or craft days. Or join an online chat group about the craft that interests you. "You want to find others who share your excitement about your projects," says Ericson. "This is the kind of connection that feeds your soul." Alternatively, start crafting with your kids. Have a weekly or monthly craft night for the whole family. Plan crafting activities around holidays: Halloween (carving pumpkins, of course!), Thanksgiving, Christmas, and Chanukah—even Valentine's Day. One of my happiest personal memories is of Wednesday afternoons after school, when my mother and I would spend an hour together doing crafts. This was my time alone with her, and we shared it by making needlepoint pillows, sewing, coloring, drawing, or playing games. This time laid the groundwork for me to become the crafter I am today and forged a lifelong connection between us.

As a final note of caution, McMeekin advises choosing the people you show your crafts to carefully. After all, you're sharing a piece of your soul. "There are vultures and saboteurs on the loose—they may even be in your own house—who will try to shame you about your work and convince you it's not good enough. Don't believe them," she says. Protect your ego—and always remember that your work is about self-expression and you. It doesn't matter what others think of it, especially if their opinion inhibits you from continuing to craft. Above all, the craft is the thing.

"As we become
older, art and life
become the same
thing."

—Georges Braque

NOTE: For the names of crafts schools and organizations, see Appendix.

Healing Lesson

Taking classes is an excellent way to
acquire new skills and find like-minded
friends with whom to share your work.

Exercise to Stimulate Your Senses

After interviewing scores of artists for her book, *The 12 Secrets of Highly Creative Women*, Gail McMeekin found that all were avid exercisers. Physical activity helped the women to get unstuck when they were faced with creative roadblocks, and to push past ordinary and mundane ideas to arrive at unique flights of fancy and invention. Walking was the favored "sport," but other physical activities were also beneficial, she says.

"There is a vitality, a life force, an energy, a quickening that is translated through you into action, and because there is only one of you in all of time, this expression is unique. And if you block it, it will never exist through any other medium and be lost."

—Martha Graham

The good news is that the latest scientific studies bear out the idea that exercise not only pumps the body, but also the mind. And even better news is that you don't have to be an elite athlete or work so hard that you get a "runner's high" (YES!). In fact, psychological studies find that just a single bout of activity makes you feel and think better—for instance, a ten-minute walk can improve your mood for two hours, says Robert Thayer, PhD, author of *Calm Energy: How People Regulate Mood with Food and Exercise*. Regular exercise has longer-lasting mental effects: It relieves stress, anxiety, and depression (and may prevent mood problems if you work out regularly), and raises your self-esteem and self-confidence. It may even reverse some of the mental declines that can occur with aging, probably because it improves blood flow to the brain.

How Exercise Affects Your Mood and Creativity

- ✧ Calms you and energizes you at the same time
- ✧ Reduces stress
- ✧ Helps to relieve anxiety and depression
- ✧ Enhances self-esteem and confidence
- ✧ Gives you quiet time
- ✧ Improves your physical health
- ✧ Boosts your mood

Most importantly, exercise appears to help you think more clearly and allows creative insights. Theories differ about why this is so, but it seems to have something to do with the fact that exercise gives you energy and makes you more alert. Because it makes you feel happier, you're also more apt to do something creative.

Healing Lesson

Walking and other forms of exercise are great ways to unblock your creativity, think through crafting problems, and come up with new ideas and solutions. And they can provide energy for late-night crafting sessions!

Find Flow—and Your Creativity Will Follow

12

A state of complete absorption, effortless action, and intense joy. That's "flow," a term coined by Mihaly Csikszentmihalyi, PhD, author of *Flow: The Psychology of Optimal Experience*, among other books. When you're in flow, you lose track of time as you concentrate on the task at hand—a feeling akin to "being in the zone," in athletic parlance or "aesthetic rapture" in artist language. You're on a "natural high," and your intense level of concentration spurs the production of brain chemicals such as feel-good endorphins and dopamine. You are glad to be alive and feeling that life is eminently worth living. Your skills exactly match the needs of the task and you lose any feelings of self-consciousness. Your body and mind work in perfect harmony and you're in an optimal creative state.

"The intellect has little to do on the road to discovery. There comes a leap in consciousness, call it intuition or what you will, and the solution comes to you, and you don't know how or why."

—Albert Einstein

How to Get into Flow

Over the past thirty-plus years, Dr. Csikszentmihalyi has studied three thousand people to find out how they achieve flow. Sedentary activities, such as watching television and playing videogames, don't bring flow, but painting a landscape does.

More specifically, you can achieve flow by:

- Choosing an activity you're passionate about. For people like us, crafts are the answer.

- Selecting an activity that allows you to express and learn more about yourself and to develop your skills.

- Letting go and releasing yourself from the need to control the outcome.

- Matching your projects to your skill level.

- Setting goals. These benchmarks should be challenging enough to keep you interested and involved, but not impossible to achieve, says NYU psychologist Robert Reiner, PhD. "You have to push yourself a little bit to hone your skill. If the craft is too humdrum, you'll get bored and stop doing it." But if it's too hard, you'll feel anxiety, not flow, not happiness, not healing.

- Concentrating on the task. Don't watch the clock. In fact, if you really get into flow, you won't even notice the time fly by. Suddenly it will be hours later.

Let Yourself Lie Fallow Sometimes

"We owe most of our great inventions and most of the achievements of genius to idleness—either enforced or voluntary."

—Agatha Christie

The polar opposite of flow is allowing yourself not to do your craft. Sometimes you need to give yourself a break from your work, or sometimes other types of work or your life take precedence. Don't feel bad about it. Down time is essential to creativity—and you may be storing up for a breakthrough. Even when you're not doing the actual physical work of your craft, you mind and soul are continuing to hum on, working behind the scenes in search of new ideas and solutions.

Gail McMeekin says that nature always reminds her of the natural order of dormancy and blossoming. "In the creative cycles of birth and death and rebirth, there are times when we are empty of ideas, adrift in a sea of ambiguity and nothingness," she writes in *The 12 Secrets of Highly Creative Women*. "These times can be labeled the neutral zone, the void, a vacuum. No matter what they are called, they are part of the creative cycle, and wise women accept them and trust that when it's time, their inspirations will percolate again."

> "In art, the self becomes self-forgetful."
>
> —Flannery O'Connor

Healing Lesson

Flow occurs when you love what you're doing so much that you become totally absorbed in it and get total joy from it. You won't get into flow by watching TV or a video, but a craft or hobby is a sure way to bring it on.

Enjoy the Process 13

It's not the product that matters, but the process. Once you've made something, no matter how pretty, the experience is over. It's kind of like life: you want to live each day fully, because you'll never have the chance to live it over again. So rather than focusing on the end result, heed the process. "What you make is only the residue of how much fun you've had," says fabric artist Diane Ericson. The key is to revel in the task of creating—the materials, the colors, the patterns, the new ideas—rather than just mindlessly pushing to finish a project. "New work comes from play and giving yourself the opportunity to engage in open-ended process without attachment to the outcome," adds Ericson. "If you just head for the end product, you won't see certain things that could happen."

> "In any work that is truly creative, I believe, the writer cannot be omniscient in advance about the effects he proposes to produce. The suspense of a novel is not only in the reader, but in the novelist, who is intensely curious about what will happen to the hero."
>
> —Mary McCarthy

- ✧ Take frequent breaks.
- ✧ Practice play.
- ✧ Do something completely out of character.
- ✧ Start in the middle instead of the beginning of a project.
- ✧ Work in a new environment.
- ✧ Limit your supply list (limitations often produce great art since you have to figure out new ways to work with them).
- ✧ Change the way you work (for instance, don't just copy a pattern, change the design a bit) to open yourself up and pull yourself out of a rut.

By focusing on process, says Julia Cameron in *The Artist's Way*, your creative life will have a sense of adventure. "Focused on product, the same creative life can feel foolish or barren." In fact, focusing on product often leads to creative blockage, she writes, since we may worry that a new artistic pathway won't get us where we want to go in our career or won't work out the way we want it to. "The grace to be a beginner is always the best prayer for an artist. The beginner's humility and openness lead to exploration. Exploration leads to accomplishment. All of it begins at the beginning, with the first small and scary step."

"Creativity lies not in the done but in doing."

—Julia Cameron

Ericson notes that the way many people have been taught to do crafts can be inconsistent with experimentation: You buy the pattern, you read the instructions, you purchase the fabrics and notions, and you follow the rules. You sit down at the sewing machine and you sew. You don't screw around. "But God didn't write the patterns and they aren't set in stone," she says. "People are hungry for new experiences, and buying a new pattern and new fabric isn't enough. You need to stretch your imagination." So she suggests starting a new project by choosing the buttons first, and then working your fabric selection around that. Or using the same pattern for an entire year and seeing how many different things you can do with it. Or just making pockets for two weeks, and after that, deciding what you want to make from the pockets. Or if you're a strictly traditional quilter, creating a free-form or crazy quilt where you just slap one piece of fabric down on another willy-nilly and sew it together. "Start the process differently and you'll create a bigger space for yourself to work in," she advises, adding that you need to give yourself permission to *not* follow the rules and to color outside the lines. "Use a pattern as a basic guideline. Read the directions, then personalize them for yourself."

"The creation of something new is not accomplished by the intellect but by the play instinct acting from inner necessity. The creative mind plays with the objects it loves."

—Carl Jung

Healing Lesson

Enjoy the process as much as you do the final product. To twist Shakespeare's words a bit, "The play's the thing." Stretch your creativity by starting your usual process in a new and exciting way, giving yourself a bigger mental space to work in.

Forget Perfection 14

Sometimes, despite your best efforts, your seams don't match, your poems don't sing, and your paints run. That can be disappointing and depressing (I call it "the agony of crafting"), but it's all part of the learning process that can lead to bigger and better things. "You have to practice to get good at a craft," says quilter and composer Ricky Tims. "It's a developed skill, just like playing an instrument. The most important thing is to do your best—you don't want to do sloppy work—be proud of your accomplishments, and look forward to doing better."

"Anyone who has never made a mistake has never tried anything new."

—Albert Einstein

The fact is that you do want your craft to challenge you. But you don't want to make yourself crazy over an outcome gone awry. Perfection isn't the goal here (or actually anywhere, since to be human means to be imperfect). Even though we know perfection isn't really possible, many crafters—myself included—tend to beat themselves up if they do a less-than-stellar job. The result is they negate the benefits of expressing themselves and working with their hands. "You've got to give yourself permission to be imperfect and to play," advises fabric artist Diane Ericson. "If you have to make a project just right, you set yourself up with just one more chore to accomplish. You lose the joy."

Quilter and teacher Lura Schwarz Smith adds, "It is a real challenge for many people to allow themselves the pleasure of creating without being terribly judgmental about their own work. Every one of us has an individual voice of creativity like no one else's, and the pure, simple joy of the creative act is one of the most rewarding things on the planet."

"The seed for your next art work lies embedded in the imperfections of your current piece."

—David Bayles and Ted Orland, Art & Fear

In her classes, Schwarz Smith outlaws statements such as "I can't draw" and "I'm not creative," which she believes are crippling to the creative nature. "They're like stepping on the brake and the gas pedal at once," she says. "You aren't going to get very far down the road that way! If you can give your very best effort to each project, and know that you are doing the best you can at that moment, at whatever stage of expertise you have at that time, you can best allow yourself the pleasure of the creative process. When the project is completed, you should appreciate the learning experience, enjoy that very best effort, and then move on to the next. Let it go."

Coach and author Gail McMeekin says that we need to move away from our old-school training of evaluating artwork as good or bad. We need to have realistic expectations of ourselves, especially if we're beginners, about what we can accomplish. "As we progress, we're going to have positive periods and stuck periods, and we're going to move in cycles of flow. Creating without censoring is always a catalyst for stretching further."

"The owner must keep his mouth shut when his work starts to speak."

—Friedrich Nietzsche

If you suffer from a negative attitude toward your crafting, fearing it's not good enough or as special as others' work (something I struggle with constantly), heed this advice so you can not only do work that is truly creative but also push through your fear of failure: "Personal permission is key here," says Gail McMeekin. "Successful people fail regularly and then move on. Unsuccessful people get paralyzed by their lack of positive outcome and run and hide. Failure is part of experimentation. When we say to ourselves 'what if I painted this beach midnight blue?' we are taking a risk. That beach may look awesome or terrible. If it looks terrible, then we paint it another color—we don't decide that we are lousy painters." Fear is always a possible choice when we are in a creative mode, adds McMeekin, but it is a stifling one. "We must learn how to coexist with fear so we push our creative efforts to further heights."

Adds Lura Schwarz Smith, "Don't apologize to yourself or anyone else if your effort doesn't satisfy you completely. It's all part of the process of creative growth, and seeking to do better can be a powerful tool rather than an impediment. Trust the process and begin with what you have and where you are, and grow from there." And remember, not taking a risk is actually taking a risk, too.

> "Ever tried? Ever failed? No matter.
> Try again. Fail again. Fail better."
>
> —Samuel Beckett

Healing Lesson

Challenge yourself with your craft,
but don't ruin the fun by being a
perfectionist. Every mistake takes you
a step further on the creative path and
teaches you new things. Being afraid
to make mistakes...that's making a
mistake too.

Not a Comparer Be 15

I've always been a comparer. Who has more than me, who has less? Who's better, who's worse? Who's more successful, who's less? And always: where do I stand on the continuum? I even compare my quilting, so that when I look at the spectacular works of other quilters I sometimes want to cry. I know I'll never be as good. Instead of inspiring me, I allow their quilts to make me feel like a less-than. For the longest time, I even refused to show my quilts to others, sure that they would ridicule them for their poor craftsmanship, or for my not having done them the "right" way. I was always afraid of being found out for not measuring up to snuff. But somewhere in the last year or two, I've turned a corner. I've realized that I've been giving other people—whether they wanted it or not—too much power over me by putting my self-esteem in their hands. Finally, I've come close to really embracing the old cliché that it doesn't matter what other people think, it only matters what I think of my work, and whether my work works for me. I quilt because it brings me joy, because I love the way the fabrics look when placed in juxtaposition, the interplay of the threads and the fibers, and creating something out of raw materials. I love having a craft that let's me express what's inside. What's more, I've realized that most people couldn't care

> "There ain't no rules around here! We're trying to accomplish something!"
>
> —Thomas Edison

less if I do good work or bad. They are far more interested in their own work and growing it than making judgments about what I do. And even if they are making judgments, what other people think of me is none of my business, as Mary Tyler Moore was once quoted as saying.

"We can secure other people's approval if we do right and try hard; but our own is worth a hundred of it, and no way has been found of securing that."

—Mark Twain

"It can be deadly to compare your work to that of others," warns fiber artist and coach Diane Ericson. "That puts a damper on both your creativity and your enjoyment. Remember, you're on your own journey."

One of the problems is that many people expect to be able to do a craft well, right from the beginning. But you need to give yourself time to learn a technical skill and to master different media, says Ericson. "Most people don't draw—which is not to say that they *can't* draw. There is a direct relationship between how much time you spend doing a craft and what you're good at. You can't be a master right off the bat."

Another part of the problem may be how you originally learned to do artwork. You were probably told in school to follow the directions and do what everybody else did. And if you colored outside the lines or drew an abstract image when a realistic image was called for, you might have been chastised. So unconsciously, today you may believe that there is only one right way to do art—and if you're like me, you often think you're doing it the wrong way. Not because you don't want to do it the right way, but because you're technically not capable of doing it that way. Or, again like me, you may feel that you're not capable of going to the outer reaches the way some special, really original artists do, to make something that is truly unique.

Coach and author Gail McMeekin feels that her love of art was "slaughtered by a cruel art teacher" in childhood. "When I was in junior high school, I was in an art class with many talented people," remembers McMeekin. "My teacher was a well-known artist in the community and on television, and she adored the students with real artistic talent and ignored the rest of us most of the time. When we did ceramics, I made my mother a blue and white curvy ashtray. I thought the ashtray came out of the kiln looking pretty good, considering my lack of talent." Gail told her teacher that she was pleased and planned to give the ashtray to her mother for Mother's Day. When the teacher acted as if Gail was kidding, she was mortified. "This was a Friday afternoon and I didn't have another present for my mother. So I did give it to my mother and it was on our coffee table for years. But I felt totally humiliated by this 'saboteur' and was thrilled that I could drop art as an elective the next year." As a result of this experience, McMeekin abandoned art for many years thinking she didn't have the ability. "I just assumed that I was uncreative and stopped playing at it until I took a watercolor class. Now I relish painting and the play of it all. I just let it happen and leave my judgments at the door. I especially love doing watercolors on tiles

"Be yourself. The world worships the original."

—Jean Cocteau

because I can just erase a painting in a flash and start over."

When reviewing your work, rather than labeling it good or bad, instead ask yourself, "What feeling am I trying to convey with this piece?" advises sewing artist Marcy Tilton. Don't judge the artistic merits of the piece, but rather focus on the emotional merits and your intention in making it.

"I must have come from a long line of strugglers. Maybe I will always struggle. But once I accept the part I can't control, I stop struggling with struggle, I have choices. When I accept my limits, there's a wide range of possibilities I can tap into."

—Sue Bender, Stretching Lessons

Perhaps the key to learning to let your work stand on its own is to stop comparing your work to the "ideal" work in your head, and letting your inner critic (that left brain butting in before your right brain gets a chance to create) get the better of you. Instead, let fly your creative intentions, instincts, and intuitions when you craft, discovering as you go and letting the work guide you instead of letting the image of someone else's work do so. Give yourself permission to do whatever you want instead of following the rules. (One of the greatest things about quilting today, and many other craft forms, is that the rules are broadening so that anything now goes. Where once it was considered bad form to have raw edges on a quilt, it's now considered okay. Asymmetry is actually admired and seams don't have to be straight. Technique is still important, as is good, careful work, but if you're not good at one technique—like setting in seams—you can opt to do something else.)

The lesson here is that instead of measuring yourself against someone else's yardstick, find inspiration in the work of others. Do your craft for yourself and yourself alone, so you preserve the fun and satisfaction and reduce the anxiety of performing for others.

Healing Lesson

Don't compare your work to the work of others, especially if you're a beginner. Try to be inspired by others' crafts, but don't shoot yourself in the foot because you're not as good. Let yourself be wherever you are on your creative journey. And do your craft for yourself and yourself alone.

Be Bold—and Bare Your Soul

"Leap, and the net will appear."

—Julia Cameron, The Artist's Way

With your art and craft, you can go anywhere, do anything, be anything. It's up to you to set the route. But the only way to benefit maximally from crafting is to take a risk, make yourself vulnerable, and allow your work to be personal and revealing. Find your path and then follow it. In that way, crafting and creativity can lead to great insights into the soul.

Your craftwork showcases your spirit and your individuality—and provides a means for you to create something tangible, as a record of your feelings, emotions, beliefs, and experiences, and even as a legacy for your children and their children. "In its simplest sense, art making is an activity that generates self-esteem, encourages risk taking and experimentation, teaches new skills, and enriches one's life," writes Cathy A. Malchiodi, in *The Art Therapy Sourcebook*. In a greater sense, it is about healing your body, mind, and spirit, and making you stronger to face life's challenges.

Carry Your Creativity with You Every Day

"Creativity isn't what you do once or twice a week—it's the way you approach your life," says fabric artist Diane Ericson. "Everyone is creative, but some people have been nurtured and some haven't.

You have to own your creativity, develop it, grow it, like a garden." Here then, are some ideas for doing just that.

- **Consider yourself a creative person in every day and every way.** As Julia Cameron, author of *The Artist's Way*, puts it, "We are created, and so we are designed to create." Creativity is a form of problem-solving, so it can apply to almost any situation in life and to your everyday occupation—in fact, the ability to creatively problem-solve is now considered a key attribute of a great employee.

- **Find your creative personality.** Relax—you don't have to search for it. "Your creative personality is already inside of you," says Tera Leigh, an artist and author of *How To Be Creative If You Never Thought You Could*. "You don't have to do anything except invite it to come out and play." Experiment to find which creative pursuits best suit your style.

- **Take your creative urges seriously.** Sue Shellenbarger, author of *The Breaking Point: How Female Midlife Crisis Is Transforming Today's Women*, encourages thinking about what truly is going to make you happy. "Go towards what gives you joy and allot time to pursue these things—an hour or two a week, at least, and hopefully more."

- **Write down or audiotape stray thoughts and dreams.** These are the seeds of great ideas—and are often lost just before or after sleep or in the rush of the day.

- **Keep a journal of your inspirations,** advises Gail McMeekin, author of *The 12 Secrets of Highly Creative Women*. Carry a small sketchbook to draw things you see or to hold swatches of fabric you like or are using in a current project.

- **Make an excitement list**, says McMeekin, so you can follow your fascinations. What attracts you and what turns on your creative fire? This is where you begin. Creativity is about experimentation, and you have to be willing to try things and then reroute them until you get the right formula.

- **Relax**, encourages Sue Bender, author of *Stretching Lessons: The Daring That Starts Within*. "At the beginning of any new challenge we encounter obstacles, confusion and doubts," she writes. "That's natural. But when we allow the rigidity within us to begin to melt, we're inviting our soul to grow wings."

- **Make "artist dates" with yourself**, advises Julia Cameron. She suggests setting aside time on a weekly basis—something like two hours a week—to nurture your inner artist. The date, which is only with you and should be solitary in nature—might consist of going to a museum or gallery, to the beach at sunrise or sunset, or out to listen to music at a local club.

- **Be kind to yourself, especially while you're learning.** "Judging your early artistic efforts is artistic abuse," says Julia Cameron. When your art doesn't turn out quite the way you envisioned it would, judging it harshly will only make you feel worse and can be undermining and demotivating, agrees psychologist Kristin Neff of the University of Texas at Austin and author of *Self-Compassion: Stop Beating Yourself Up and Leave Insecurity Behind*. Instead, be self-compassionate and accept your shortcomings and mistakes as part of being human. Self-compassion is a better motivator than self-criticism, she says, because it is grounded in love of yourself rather than fear of failure.

- **Take vacations. Really.** A survey by Expedia.com found that 49.4 million Americans don't use up all of their vacation days each year. That's actually counter-productive, because research shows that down time is not only vital to well-being, but also to creativity and work performance. Even better: Take a creative vacation, where you learn new skills or indulge in a craft or hobby. Exercising your creative muscle leads to better problem-solving.

- **Go to nature.** Most artists find the beauty of nature to be the greatest source of inspiration. Going for a walk on a country road, cupping a flower in your hand and breathing deeply of its petals, or listening to the sweet trickle of a stream brings a feeling of peace and calm that can put you in the right-brain frame of mind.

- **Get in touch with your intuition.** Go with hunches about what you should do with your projects; that will lead to play, which will lead to original work. Don't let rational thought obscure what you know without knowing how you know it.

- **Have faith in your abilities.** Persevere in your craft because you love it, and whether you ever become a master crafter or not, it will bring joy back to you ten-fold.

A Final Word

In short, go for the gusto when approaching your craft. I hope that's what this book has shown you, and that it has given you some tools for doing just that.

You already knew that you could use crafts just for fun or to relax. But now you see that if you're so inclined, you can also use crafts with intention and focus to heal yourself and develop into a more fully rounded person. That's a tall order for a hand-knit sweater, a stained-glass window, a photograph, or a painting, but one that crafts have the shoulders to carry.

Healing Lesson

The older you get, the more you realize how little most things matter in the scheme of things. So why not go for the gusto? Be bold and bare you soul—and reap the benefits of crafting, not only for your heart and mind, but for your body and soul.

Appendix

Crafting Organizations

American Art Therapy Association, Inc.
Tel: 888-290-0878
Website: www.arttherapy.org

American Craft Council
Tel: 800-836-3470
Website: www.craftcouncil.org

American Quilter's Society
Tel: 270-898-7903
Website: www.americanquilter.com

American Sewing Guild
Tel: 713-729-3000
Website: www.asg.org

American Therapeutic Recreation Association
Tel: 601-450-2872
Website: www.atra-online.org

Benson-Henry Institute for Mind Body Medicine
Tel: 617-643-6090
Website: www.massgeneral.org/bhi/deafult.aspx

Caring Crafts
Website: www.caringcrafts.com

The Church of Craft
Website: www.churchofcraft.org

Craft and Hobby Association
Consumer website: www.craftplace.org

Get Crafty
Website: www.getcrafty.com

The Knitting Guild of America
Tel: 740-452-4541
Website: www.tkga.com

Quilts, Inc.
Tel: 713-781-6864
Website: www.quilts.com

Sewing and Craft Alliance
Website: www.sewing.org

Society for the Arts in Healthcare
Tel: 202-299-9770
Website: www.thesah.org

Survivors Art Foundation
Website: www.survivorsartfoundation.org

Crafters and Experts Cited in This Book

Many of the crafters and experts cited in this book sell their work or conduct workshops. If you'd like to contact them, here's how:

Jeanne Carbonetti

A watercolor artist, teacher, and author

Jeanne is the author of the "Path of Painting" series of books (*The Tao of Watercolor, The Zen of Creative Painting, The Yoga of Drawing and Making Pearls: The True Nature of Creative Life*), as a well as a teacher and artist.

Crow Hill Gallery and the Eden Center for Creative Power

Chester, VT

Tel: 802-875-3763

Website: www.crowhillgallery.com

Connie Thanasoulis-Cerrachio

A success and career coach

Connie is co-founder of Six Figure Start, a career coaching firm in New York City, and a former Fortune-500 recruiter.

Tel: 212-501-2234

Website: www.sixfigurestart.com

Ann D. Collier, PhD

A clinical psychologist and textile handcrafter

Ann is studying the psychological benefits of textiles.

Tel: 715-836-2487

Website: www.uwec.edu/psyc/Who/collier.htm

Diane Ericson

A fabric artist, pattern designer, creativity coach, and writer

Diane has a website where you can order her patterns, notecards, and prints, find out about her workshops, and gain inspiration.

ReVisions

Tel: 541-708-5120

Website: www.dianeericson.com

Barbara Ganim

An expressive art therapist and author

Barbara is the author of three fabulous books: *Visual Journaling*, written with Susan Fox, *Art and Healing*, and *Drawing from the Heart: A Seven-Week Program to Heal Emotional Pain and Loss Through Expressive Art*

To contact her or to learn more about expressive art programs:

Expressive Art Therapy Program

Salve Regina University

100 Ochre Point Avenue

Newport, RI 02840-4192

Tel: 401-341-2157

Michelle Keating, RN, OCN, MSN

A cancer educator and MS and crafts researcher

Michelle has a website where she offers bracelets to raise money for MS awareness.

Website: www.msawarenessbeadedbangles.com

Tera Leigh

Artist, photographer, and author

Tera wrote a favorite book of mine, *How To Be Creative If You*

Websites: www.teraleigh.com and www.teras-wish.com

Gail McMeekin, MSW, LICSW

A creativity and career coach and author

Through Gail's website you can order her books, *The 12 Secrets of Highly Successful Women, The 12 Secrets of Highly Creative Women,* and *The Power of Positive Choices,* as well as audiotapes and her lovely Creativity Courage Cards, and sign up for her Creative Success newsletter. She also offers career and creativity coaching, either in person or over the phone.

Creative Success

Tel: 617-323-1442

Website: www.creativesuccess.com

Lura Schwarz Smith

An art quilter, teacher, and author

Lura's incredible quilt graces the cover of *Craft to Heal.* She accepts commissions to custom-make quilts and teaches nationwide, and sells quilts, instructional videos, and cards and prints of her quilts from her website. She is the co-author of *Secrets of Digital Quilting—From Camera to Quilt* with her husband, photographer Kerby C. Smith.

Tel: 559-683-6899

Website: www.lura-art.com

Marcy Tilton

A sewing teacher, writer, pattern designer, and coach

Marcy and Diane Ericson hold sewing and creativity retreats each year, and you can buy Marcy's patterns, fabric, CDs, and other materials from her website.

Tel: 541-592-2969

Website: www.marcytilton.com

Ricky Tims

A quilt artist and teacher, a composer/musician, and founder of *The Quilt Life* magazine with Alex Anderson

You can buy Ricky's CDs, videos, books, fabric, and patterns on his website, and find out about his teaching schedule.

Website: www.rickytims.com

Blogs, Newsletters, and Websites

Arts Enclave

Meditations on art, writing, and creativity from writer Linda Peckel.

Website: http://artsenclave.wordpress.com

Craft for Health

A joint venture of craft designer Kathy Peterson and nurse Barb Dehn, this blog features stories of crafters who've discovered the healing powers of crafts.

Website: www.craftforhealth.typepad.com

Creative Success

A website from creativity coach Gail McMeekin. You can sign up for her excellent e-newsletter on the site, as well as buy her books and inspirational cards.

Website: www.creativesuccess.com

Make Great Stuff

The brainchild of artist Sarah Bush, who offers collaging creative

breakthrough teleclasses (fun!) and blogs regularly about creative issues.
Website: www.makegreatstuff.com

Stitchlinks
A newsletter from Betsan Corkhill, a British expert who is pursuing research on the benefits of needle crafts in reducing pain and depression.
Website: www.stitchlinks.com

Craft Schools, Retreats, Festivals, Conventions, and Spas

Classes are waiting! Below are some schools, retreats, festivals, and yes, even a couple of spas and resorts you might want to check out for crafting opportunities and relaxation. (I give you fair warning, however, that I'm not personally familiar with most of these. Rather, the list is for your convenience.)

Online Guide to Art and Craft Workshops, Schools and Retreats
http://art.shawguides.com

American Quilter's Society Shows
Held in Paducah, KY, Des Moines, IA, Lancaster, PA, and Knoxville, TN
Website: www.americanquilter.com
Arrowmont School of Arts and Crafts
Tel: 865-436-5860 Website: www.arrowmont.org

Art Quilt Tahoe
Lake Tahoe, CA

Tel: 530-887-0600

Website: www.artquilttahoe.com

Augusta Heritage Center of Davis & Elkins College
Elkins, WV
Tel: 304-637-1209
Website: www.augustaheritage.com

Bead & Button Show (jewelry-making)
Milwaukee, WI
Website: www.beadandbuttonshow.com

Colorado Art Camp
Durango, CO
Tel: 970-769-0297
Website: www.coloradoartcamp.com

Craft and Hobby Association Supershow
Held in conjunction with other shows across the USA
Website: www.craftsupershow.com

Creating Keepsakes Scrapbooking Conventions
Held across the USA
Website: www.creatingkeepsakes.com

Creativ Festival
Toronto, Canada
Website: www.creativfestival.com

Design Outside the Lines (sewing and fiber retreat)
Led by Diane Ericson and Marcy Tilton, alternately held in
California, Oregon, and New Mexico
Website: www.dianeericson.com/c/Retreats/Retreats.html

Dillman's Creative Arts Foundation
Lac du Flambeau, WI
Tel: 715-588-3143
Website: www.dillmans.com

Fletcher Farm School for the Arts and Crafts
Ludlow, VT
Tel: 802-228-8770
Website: www.fletcherfarm.com

Great American Scrapbooking Conventions
Arlington, TX and Chantilly, VA
Website: www.greatamericanscrapbook.com

Indie Craft Experience
Atlanta, GA
Website: www.ice-atlanta.com

International Quilt Festival
Held in Houston, TX, Long Beach, CA, and Cincinnati, OH
Website: www.quilts.com

Learning & Products Expo: Art!
Pasadena, CA
Website: www.learningproductexpo.com

Maker Faire
Detroit, MI, Bay Area, CA and New York City events
Website: www.makerfaire.com

Miraval Resort and Spa
Tucson, AZ
Tel: 800-232-3969
Website: www.miravalresorts.com

Mohonk Mountain House
New Paltz, NY
Tel: 800-772-6646
Website: www.mohonk.com

Penland School of Crafts
Penland, NC
Tel: 828-765-2359
Website: www.penland.org

Snow Farm
The New England Craft Program
Williamsburg, MA
Tel: 413-268-3101
Website: www.snowfarm.org

Stitches (knitting)
Events held in the East, West, Midwest, and the South
Website: www.knittinguniverse.com

Where to Sell Your Crafts

Ebay

Website: www.ebay.com

Etsy

Website: www.etsy.com

Books I Love

If you're looking for creative inspiration, here are some books that have stoked my fire and that I hold dear to my heart, many of which I've cited in this, my own, book...

Art & Fear: Observations on the Perils (and Rewards) of Artmaking
David Bayles and Ted Orland

If you were to buy just one book for your creative library, this would be it. *Art & Fear* inspires and motivates! It's all about the art process—the way art gets made, the fears that keep it from getting made, and some of our pervasive cultural assumptions about artists (like being born with talent is the only route to good art).

The 12 Secrets of Highly Creative Women: A Portable Mentor *The Power of Positive Choices*
Gail McMeekin

These are two of my favorite books by a creativity and career coach and therapist—and a third is coming soon, *The 12 Secrets of Highly Successful Women*, along with a creativity workbook. The first 12 Secrets book is filled with fabulous nuggets of advice and wisdom from women who have pursued creative paths in all walks of life, as well as exercises to help you awaken your own creativity. The Positive Choices book addresses how to make your life better by subtracting negative aspects and adding positive choices.

The Artist's Way: A Spiritual Path to Higher Creativity
Julia Cameron

The bible on creativity by the guru of creativity. Julia Cameron's fabulous book teaches you how to get past creative blockages (and she thinks we're all blocked to one extent or another). The book contains a 12-week self-motivated program in discovering and recovering your creative self, as well as suggestions for starting an "Artist's Way" group.

Creative Healing: How to Heal Yourself by Tapping Your Hidden Creativity
Michael Samuels, MD, and Mary Rockwood Lane, RN, MSN

A medically based book on the healing powers of the arts that teaches you how to find your "inner artist-healer." It describes the history of art and healing, covers techniques for using art, writing, dance, and music to heal yourself, as well as how professional artists use art to heal themselves and others.

Self-Compassion: Stop Beating Yourself Up and Leave Insecurity Behind
Kristin Neff, PhD

Psychologist Neff, borrowing heavily from Buddhism, makes the case for abandoning the quest for high self-esteem and its attendant goals to be perfect, number 1, and better than everyone else in favor of being human, being connected, and accepting our limitations and weaknesses. Instead of berating yourself for making mistakes, she advises treating yourself as compassionately as you would a friend. Research shows that self-compassion leads to greater motivation, less anxiety and depression, and ultimately greater happiness. People who are self-compassionate lead healthier, more productive lives than those who are self-critical; they're also better able to get up when they fall than people who are self-critical.

Self-Nurture: Learning to Care for Yourself as Effectively as You Care for Everyone Else
Alice Domar, PhD, and Henry Dreher

This book by a preeminent mind-body psychologist focuses on reducing stress and reconstructing your life so you care for yourself better. There's a great section on bringing play and creativity into your life.

The Tao of Watercolor: A Revolutionary Approach to the Practice of Painting; The Zen of Creative Painting: An Elegant Design for Revealing Your Muse; The Yoga of Drawing: Uniting Body, Mind and Spirit in the Art of Drawing and Making Pearls: The True Nature of Creative Life
Jeanne Carbonetti

If you think you can't draw or paint, try one of these books. Jeanne has come up with some unique techniques for accessing your natural artistic style—instead of fighting it in an effort to make your art conform to traditional standards—using the mind-body principles of Zen and the Tao.

Visual Journaling: Going Deeper Than Words
Barbara Ganim and Susan Fox

A fabulous workbook that contains the wisdom of expressive art therapists and teaches you how to use journal drawings to access your internal thoughts and feelings and release stress. It contains a 6-week program you can follow on your own or in a group.

Art and Healing: Using Expressive Art to Heal Your Body, Mind, and Spirit
Barbara Ganim

A truly unique book that gathers much of the scientific work done on the healing power of expressive art therapy and explains it to the layperson. The book describes the ways in which creating art can produce emotional and physical benefits for those involved in the process and those who view it. It teaches readers how to express negative, painful, and repressed emotions and deal with serious illnesses through art therapy techniques, exercises, and visualizations.

The Knitting Sutra: Craft As a Spiritual Practice
Susan Gordon Lydon

This charming book of essays likens knitting to meditation, and describes it as one key to spiritual enlightenment.

Stretching Lessons: The Daring That Starts from Within
Sue Bender

A lovely little book about the author's quest to grow her soul beyond her self-imposed limits ... to stretch and become "bigger than."

No More Secondhand Art: Awakening the Artist Within
Peter London

An interesting, somewhat academic, book on finding the originality and artist within you.

Drawing on the Right Side of the Brain
Betty Edwards

A now-classic volume that uses split-brain research to show even the most logical among us how to tap into our drawing ability by accessing the right side of the brain.

Your Creative Brain: Seven Steps to Maximize Imagination, Productivity, and Innovation in Your Life
Shelly Carson, PhD

Dr. Carson is a researcher and teacher at Harvard University who has come up with the "CREATES" model, a set of seven different brain activation patterns that she believes come into play during different aspects of the creative process. The book has a series of quizzes to help you isolate your personal creative brain patterns, and suggestions on how to expand your creativity and therefore your productivity. (PS: Because of the scoring system for the quizzes, I recommend buying a hard copy of this book and not an electronic version.)

How To Be Creative If You Never Thought You Could
Tera Leigh

This is a very non-intimidating and fun book of inspiration and easy projects for people who want to try different crafts.

Taking Flight: Inspiration and Techniques to Give Your Creative Spirit Wings
Kelly Rae Roberts
and
Mixed-Media Self-Portraits
Cate Coulacos Prato

These are both mixed-media books filled with fun projects, inspiration, and techniques.

Creative Awakenings: Envisioning the Life of Your Dreams Through Art
Sheri Gaynor

I really enjoy this book—it's filled with mixed-media techniques that help you use art to set your intentions and create a "Book-of-Dreams Journal."

About the Author

Nancy Monson is a nationally recognized freelance magazine and book writer who specializes in the topics of crafts and creativity, health, nutrition, and psychology. Her articles have been published in over 30 major national magazines, including *Family Circle, First for Women, Glamour, More, Reader's Digest, Redbook, Shape, Weight Watchers Magazine,* and *Woman's Day.* Her previous books include the *Smart Guide to Boosting Your Energy* and *Just What the Doctor Ordered: An Insider's Guide to Medical Writing* (an ebook she co-authored that is available at www.medicalwritingbook.com). She also writes continuing medical education materials for healthcare providers.

Nancy has been a crafter since she was a child and has been an avid quilter and mixed-media collager for the past two decades.

She has spoken to the Craft and Hobby Association and other organizations about the therapeutic benefits of crafts, and appeared as a craft expert on numerous television and radio programs nationwide. She is available for interviews, speaking engagements, and to conduct Craft to Heal workshops.

Visit her website at www.nancymonson.com.

CPSIA information can be obtained at www.ICGtesting.com
Printed in the USA
237283LV00001B/5/P